EVALUATION AND EDUCATION
OF
CHILDREN WITH BRAIN DAMAGE

Publication Number 702

AMERICAN LECTURE SERIES®

A Monograph in

The BANNERSTONE DIVISION *of*
AMERICAN LECTURES IN SPEECH AND HEARING

Edited by

ROBERT WEST, Ph.D.
Director
Speech and Hearing Center
Brooklyn College
Brooklyn, New York

Second Printing

EVALUATION AND EDUCATION
OF
CHILDREN WITH BRAIN DAMAGE

Edited by

MORTON BORTNER, Ph.D.

Kennedy Foundation Scholar and Associate Professor
Department of Special Education
Ferkauf Graduate School of Humanities and Social Sciences
Yeshiva University
New York, New York

CHARLES C THOMAS • PUBLISHER
Springfield • Illinois • U.S.A.

1114

Published and Distributed Throughout the World by

CHARLES C THOMAS • PUBLISHER

BANNERSTONE HOUSE

301-327 East Lawrence Avenue, Springfield, Illinois, U.S.A.

NATCHEZ PLANTATION HOUSE

735 North Atlantic Boulevard, Fort Lauderdale, Florida, U.S.A.

With THOMAS BOOKS *careful attention is given to all details of manufacturing and design. It is the Publisher's desire to present books that are satisfactory as to their physical qualities and artistic possibilities and appropriate for their particular use.* THOMAS BOOKS *will be true to those laws of quality that assure a good name and good will.*

First Edition, First Printing, 1968

First Edition, Second Printing, 1970

Printed in the United States of America

N-1

CONTRIBUTORS

BIRCH, HERBERT G., M.D., Ph.D., Research Professor, Department of Pediatrics, Center for Normal and Aberrant Behavioral Development, Albert Einstein College of Medicine, Yeshiva University.

BONIFACE, WILLIAM R., M.D., Assistant Professor, Departments of Neurology and Psychiatry, University of Cincinnati College of Medicine.

BORTNER, MORTON, Ph.D., Kennedy Foundation Scholar and Associate Professor, Department of Special Education, Ferkauf Graduate School of Humanities and Social Sciences, Yeshiva University.

CHESS, STELLA, M.D., Associate Professor, Department of Psychiatry, New York University School of Medicine.

FROSTIG, MARIANNE, Ph.D., Executive Director, Marianne Frostig Center of Educational Therapy, and Clinical Professor of Education, University of Southern California.

KEPHART, NEWELL C., Ph.D., Executive Director, Achievement Center for Children, Department of Education, Purdue University.

MYSAK, EDWARD D., Ph.D., Professor and Chairman, Department of Speech Pathology and Audiology, and Director of the Speech and Hearing Center, Teachers College, Columbia University.

PATTERSON, RUTH M., Ph.D., Director, Research Project #50, Columbus State School, Columbus, Ohio.

WEINER, BLUMA B., Ed.D., Associate Professor, Department of Special Education, Ferkauf Graduate School of Humanities and Social Sciences, Yeshiva University.

ZANER, ANNETTE R., M.A., Supervisor of Clinical Services, Mount Carmel Guild Diagnostic Center for Hearing and Speech Disorders, Newark, New Jersey, and Lecturer, Seton Hall University.

ACKNOWLEDGMENTS

IT IS A PLEASURE TO acknowledge my gratitude to the Joseph P. Kennedy, Jr. Foundation whose support enabled me to work on this book; to Dr. Herbert G. Birch, friend and teacher, who introduced me to this field, whose creative thinking and research have been a constant source of inspiration; and to my father David for providing other sources of inspiration. He was very much in favor of books.

M. B.

PREFACE

T HIS BOOK IS DIVIDED INTO two parts because it has two related goals. The first is to tell the reader what different professional disciplines look for and what they consider important when evaluating brain-injured children. The disciplines represented include: speech and language, hearing, psychology, psychiatry and neurology. The second goal is to bring together in the same place, some representative strategies for the education of brain-injured children.

These goals seem desirable for the following reasons: First, there is value in introducing the thinking of various disciplines to one another. One might expect that the interdisciplinary meeting itself is the logical place for this to happen. However, not all settings are interdisciplinary, and those that are do not necessarily have the same opportunities for communication. When members of each discipline learn about the thinking of others, it happens in different ways, influences to different degrees and occurs in different places. Part One of this book deals with this problem by presenting some contemporary thinking, representative of a variety of disciplines, on the problem of evaluation of brain-injured children.

Second, it is appropriate while thinking about evaluation to wonder where this information will lead. For teachers the question is: what is the relationship of evaluation to teaching strategy? Presumably, if we know enough about what is wrong, then we are in a position to do something about it. Since the efficacy of this assumption remains to be demonstrated insofar as the education of brain-injured children is concerned, there may be value in bringing together in one book conclusions deriving both from a consideration of evaluation and of teaching strategy. The reader can decide whether the relationship between evaluation and instruction is a good one by looking for points of contact between what is said in Parts One and Two.

Third, it has become clear that consensus as to proper instructional procedures for brain-injured children is nowhere on the horizon. Therefore, there may be value in presenting the reader, especially the teacher, with a variety of strategies presently available. Thus he may choose that approach or those aspects of several approaches most congenial to him.

Since uniformity does not yet exist in the use of the term "brain-injury," it is still appropriate for statements from different disciplines and educators to emphasize different viewpoints, as long as we know their frames of reference and their definitions. No attempt has been made to introduce uniformity of usage at this time since neither research nor clinical practice is yet organized along such lines. Until this happens it remains necessary for the existing variety of viewpoints to be reflected.

MORTON BORTNER

CONTENTS

		Page
Acknowledgments	....	vii
Preface	....	ix

INTRODUCTION — BRAIN DAMAGE: AN EDUCATIONAL CATE-
GORY? — *Herbert G. Birch* and *Morton Bortner* 3

PART ONE

EVALUATION

Chapter
I. DISORDERS OF ORAL COMMUNICATION — *Edward D. Mysak* . 15
II. HEARING IMPAIRMENT — *Annette R. Zaner* 44
III. PSYCHOLOGICAL DEFICIT — *Morton Bortner* 64
IV. PSYCHIATRIC FACTORS — *Stella Chess* 95
V. NEUROLOGICAL CONSIDERATIONS — *William R. Boniface* ... 109

PART TWO

EDUCATIONAL STRATEGIES

VI. THE EDUCATIONAL METHODS OF STRAUSS AND LEHTINEN —
Morton Bortner 131
VII. TEACHING THE CHILD WITH A PERCEPTUAL-MOTOR HANDICAP
— *Newell C. Kephart* 147
VIII. EDUCATIONAL METHODS BASED ON THE GELLNER CONCEPTS OF
NEUROLOGICAL DEFICIT — *Ruth M. Patterson* 193
IX. A TREATMENT PROGRAM FOR CHILDREN WITH LEARNING DIF-
FICULTIES — *Marianne Frostig* 223
X. CURRICULUM DEVELOPMENT FOR CHILDREN WITH BRAIN DAM-
AGE — *Bluma B. Weiner* 243

EVALUATION AND EDUCATION
OF
CHILDREN WITH BRAIN DAMAGE

INTRODUCTION

BRAIN DAMAGE: AN EDUCATIONAL CATEGORY?

HERBERT G. BIRCH
MORTON BORTNER

OVER THE YEARS IT HAS become clear that the diagnostic and administrative label of "minimal brain-damage" has been increasingly extended to embrace a wide range of children who are characterized neither by a common body of symptomatology nor by identical etiologies for their dysfunctions. The spectrum of disorders designated as "brain damaged" has ranged from relatively circumscribed, specific disabilities in motor, sensory and behavioral organization to profound disturbances in behavior and intellect even, in some cases, manifested as frank psychosis.

In an attempt to bring some order to an area characterized by such a diversity of meanings, a group sponsored by the National Institute of Neurological Diseases and Blindness of the National Institutes of Health, and the National Society for Crippled Children and Adults, Inc.[6] organized a review of the literature dealing with brain damage in children. Its first task was the identification of the variety of behavioral characteristics, medical indicators and suggestions as to natural history which have shared the common label of "minimal brain damage." No less than ninety-nine signs and symptoms were compiled. Some of these signs were quite general in nature and presumably subsumed several varieties of behavior. For example, the description "possibly anti-social behavior" is not a single symptom, and its more detailed statement would raise the number of identifiable signs and symptoms to well over the hundred mark. It was not uncommon to find paradoxes among the many studies reviewed, with opposite characteristics attributed as defining the same *entity*. For example, in one study, brain-damaged children were described as *fearless* but in another as *phobic*.

Clearly, if the term "minimal brain damage" is to retain any usefulness either in clinical practice or research, it must gain increased specificity of reference. Such specificity can of course be achieved arbitrarily. But if this is done, the danger exists of neatly defining a set of criteria and characteristics which are possessed by no single child. It may perhaps be better defined in a more functionally useful manner, by re-examining the origins of the term and its realms of application. Through such historical analysis, it may be possible to induce an entity which has pertinence to clinical practice, educational policy, and research. This path appears to be attractive and will serve as a starting point for our introductory comments.

The origins of the term "minimal brain damage" are best-appreciated in the light of the efforts, made in the 1920's and 1930's, to better classify different types of intellectual aberration. During this period relatively undifferentiated institutional populations of mentally defective children came to be considered as heterogeneous aggregations within which it was necessary for administrative, clinical, and research purposes to develop meaningful subgroupings. In the course of these efforts, the designations *dementia praecox, familial, cultural, educable, and trainable retardation, autism, childhood schizophrenia, primary and secondary amentia,* and others came to be applied by evidence of symptom or etiology to more or less clearly defined subsegments of the aberrantly functioning population. It is clear from the terms used that at least two sets of criteria were being tacitly accepted for the purposes of differentiation. The first of these was symptomatologic and resulted in the differentiation of defectively functioning children either in terms of severity of intellectual defect, or in terms of associated patterns of behavioral or neurological dysfunction. The second basis for differentiation was etiologic and directed attention to genetic background, developmental environment, or to conditions of risk of damage to the central nervous system as causes for defective functioning. The term "minimal brain damage" stems from this second basis for differentiation. However, symptoms and causes were never fully separated and remain intertwined to the present day.

During the 1930's Strauss and Werner, working with populations of mentally subnormal children, increasingly came to identify two groups on a *symptomatologic* basis. One of these groups was characterized by its relative homogeneity and ubiquity of intellectual defect and the second group by the unevenness of its intellectual functioning. In addition, the second group appeared to be particularly characterized by associated behavioral disturbances including hyperkinesis, perceptual-motor incompetence, perseverative tendencies, distractibility, emotional lability, cognitive concreteness, and excessive fluidity of thinking. An analysis of the clinical histories of the two broad types of patients resulted in the preliminary finding of an excessive exposure to conditions of risk of central nervous system damage (e.g., anoxia, toxemia, prematurity, and birth-trauma) in the unevenly functioning group, and an excessive history of subnormality in the families and sibships of the individuals with more uniform intellectual deficit. These findings led to a tendency to name the symptom group with greater evidence of external risk of central nervous system damage, "exogenously" retarded; the other group with evidence suggestive of a presumed familial basis for intellectual dysfunction was termed "endogenously" retarded. It was a short step from the assumption of etiological difference based on weak historical evidence to the further assumption that the "exogenous" group was in fact brain damaged and the "endogenous" group was not. Etiology was thus attached to symptom and history. This fusion of levels has underlain our confusions to this day. Children have been classified as "brain damaged" in some studies on purely symptomatologic grounds and in other studies on the basis of having been at early risk of central nervous system damage. In still others they have been classified on the basis of independent evidence of damage to the brain whether behavioral symptoms fitting the stereotype were present or not. Even within a single set of studies the same investigators have, on occasion, utilized varying criteria for designation. Thus, Strauss in his first volume[10] was concerned largely with children *without* motor impairment, but in his second volume[11] he included the motor handicap. We thus have a literature characterized by what appears to be substantive differences in view, but which may really reflect irrelevant comparisons made by investigators who are using the same categorical label to embrace vastly different groups of children.

Clearly, in practice, the two criteria of etiology and symptomatology are not entirely separate as criteria for differential diagnosis. In fact, not only do both factors contribute to differentiation among clinical entities, but also they are intimately associated in the thinking of the examiner with other often unstated criteria relating to pathogenesis, response to treatment, and natural history. In summary, then, systematic criteria for differential diagnosis incorporating five essential steps — symptomatology, etiology, pathogenesis, treatment response and outcome — have been used only fragmentally, if at all, in defining "brain damage."

The classification "exogenous" can best be viewed as subsuming a combination of etiologic and behavioral factors in which the specific contribution of any factor to diagnosis is variable for different children or groups. Moreover, these factors are not always mutually self-supporting; e.g., positive evidence of neurological insult is not always accompanied by the presence of positive behavioral symptoms. In many cases neurological signs on medical examination are accompanied by behavioral signs on psychological examination which are within normal limits. This is illustrated in a recent study[4] which was concerned with the relationships of a variety of biological, psychological, and educational factors. Approximately 50 per cent of those children with central nervous system damage, identified by independent clinical neurologic examination, did not display any of the major behavioral signs commonly associated with exogeneity. Moreover, there is nothing mutually exclusive about a history of retardation in other members of the family and the possibility of neurological damage before, during, or after birth. This last point is clearly illustrated in the study by Feldman[7] who, in the course of selecting a familial and non-familial group for later psychological study, administered a standard neurological examination to all individuals in both groups. These two groups clearly dichotomized on the basis of history; i.e. family incidence of retardation, were not distinguishable on the basis of the frequency with which positive neurological signs were found.

If it is difficult to achieve consensus as to the neurologic and behavioral characteristics needed for the diagnostic identification of a "brain-damaged child," is it possible to define such a child for educational purposes? Gallagher,[8] among others, has argued that the educational characteristics of so-called brain-damaged children are as heterogeneous as are their psychological characteristics, and that no single instructional strategy or teaching style is generally applicable. Rather what appears to be required is individual tutoring tailored to meet the specific behavioral characteristics and educational requirements of each child as a learner.

Despite these findings, a number of educational methods have been developed with the objective of devising effective techniques for the schooling of children with behavioral symptoms of hyperkinesis, distractibility, emotional lability, perceptual immaturity and aberration, and certain types of cognitive organization. Children with such symptoms have been called "minimally brain-damaged" by school systems, and the special classes to which they are assigned have been termed "classes for brain-injured children." The school authorities having used the term "brain," for legal reasons, had to establish medical criteria for identifying the children for whom such special education would be available. The criteria had to be medical, and evidence of a damaged brain had to be identified by a physician. Ironically, many children for whom such classes are appropriate may be excluded, since other than behavioral symptoms frequently cannot be found, and there is an absence of independent medical evidence of brain-damage. Clearly, the confusion of symptoms and causes has resulted in both selective and administrative approaches which are less than optimal.

Having indicated several factors which tend to perpetuate a state of confusion, we may now ask how the problems consequent to this confusion can be resolved. The first step in such a resolution is to consider the relationship between etiology and symptomatology. The second is to recognize that independent and quite different value attaches to each of these two factors in defining a course of effective educational action.

It must first be understood that damage to the brain, minimal or otherwise, may have *many* consequences. These consequences depend, among other variables, upon the region injured, the extent of the damage, the rate at which the damage has occurred, the time in life at which it was sustained, and the physiological nature of the lesion. Damage to certain parts of the brain may be entirely asymptomatic; damage to other parts may be reflected in circumscribed sensory or motor deficits; and damage in still other parts of the brain may result in widespread inhibition, disinhibition, attentional deficits, emotional reactions, motivational changes, or other general consequences which modify functioning. The *fact* of brain damage therefore does not define the character of the behavioral symptom or the educational problem. When the consequence is general and widespread, it may still be varied in its expression and range from simple mental defect, accompanied or unaccompanied by motor dysfunctions, to totally disorganizing behavioral disorders. It is somewhere within this broad range of consequences that the so-called syndrome of the brain damaged child may have a place.

It should be recognized that children with this syndrome do not come to our notice because they have damaged brains, rather, they come to attention because they represent individuals with behaviors that are deviant and because they are unresponsive to usual methods of rearing, training, and education. Whether or not independent anatomic or physiologic evidence can be adduced to demonstrate the *fact* of brain damage is a question that is often irrelevant for symptom management and educational placement or strategy. Such evidence would only become relevant for these issues if special methods of rearing, training and education existed which were more or less efficacious for management in accordance with the *fact* of the brain damage. For the symptom complex we are considering, no such special pertinence attaches to the demonstration of etiology. We are instead at a point in the development of knowledge where the behavioral characteristics of the child and his responses to planned intervention, rather than the etiology of his disorder, determine our practices. Historically, then, our approach in education is at a stage of development not different from that of the medical management of infectious disease in the prebacterial, pre-antibiotic, and preimmunologic periods. At such a level of knowledge, etiology is of importance for prophylaxis rather than for treatment. For example, having defined obstetrical and environmental conditions of risk capable of producing undesirable behavioral syndromes, we can most certainly argue for the removal of these risk conditions. To do this, however, is a matter of prevention and is entirely different from expecting that knowledge of the conditions of risk can determine the method of child treatment. The confusion of these two levels of reasoning and of action, one stemming from knowledge of etiology and the other stemming from knowledge of symptom disorder or behavior pattern, is the source of most of our difficulties in planning for the education and management of behaviorally aberrant children.

The resolution of the dilemma of how to educate such children is suggested by the above considerations and implies that from the functional and educational point of view, our starting point at present must not be *etiology* but rather *those behavioral characteristics which define the child as a learner and social organism.* However, even this statement cannot be more than a mere guidepost with suggestive implications for the educator. It would be all too easy to assume that accurate, descriptive behavioral data lead directly, as in a logical imperative, to successful educational intervention. Such imperatives remain to be invented and demonstrated.

This position, which sets our task as that of defining the child as a learner and social organism, places the responsibility for educational designation where it belongs — with the educator. It makes it impossible for him to turn to often irrelevant medical authority in making educational decisions. It further requires that the syndrome of behavior must be clearly and functionally defined in a *behavioral* and *educational* sense to permit correct pupil assignment.

How may this objective be accomplished? One approach is through the development of "educational categories" which may come from the description of defectively functioning children in terms that are educationally pertinent. A partial answer to what may be educationally pertinent is implied in the preceding discussion and also in those studies which have dealt with such issues as sensory dominance,[9] intersensory equivalence and integration,[1,2] perceptual[5] and conceptual adequacies,[3] and a variety of other behavioral indices. In large part, the significance of these studies, which were not always directed at educational questions, appears to derive precisely from their relevance to the educational process. Such studies are relevant because they are concerned concretely with the child's mode of responsiveness and not abstractly with the intactness of his brain. The identification of modes of responsiveness is a necessary and unavoidable first step for educators seeking to establish meaningful categories upon which to base special class placement and instructional procedures.

The present volume surveys some of the background data that may permit a transition to occur from older, irrelevant categories to educationally more pertinent categories, and thereby convert special classes for "brain-injured" children from an administrative wastebasket into an effective educational facility for a functionally defined group of children. It is to be hoped that it makes some contribution to achieving this objective.

REFERENCES

1. Birch, H. G., and Lefford, A.: Intersensory development in children. *Monogr Soc Res Child Develop, 28*:89, 1963.
2. Birch, H. G. (Ed.) : *Brain Damage in Children*. Baltimore, Williams & Wilkins, 1964.
3. Birch, H. G., and Bortner, M.: Stimulus competition and category usage in normal children. *J Genet Psychol, 109*:195-204, 1966.
4. Birch, H. G.: *Epidemiology of Mental Subnormality*, in preparation.
5. Bortner, M., and Birch, H. G.: Perceptual and perceptual-motor dissociation in cerebral palsied children. *J Nerv Ment Dis, 134*:103-108, 1962.
6. Clements, S. D.: *Minimal Brain Dysfunction in Children*. Dept. of Health, Education and Welfare, Public Health Service Publication No. 1415, 1966.
7. Feldman, I. S.: Psychological differences among moron and borderline mental defectives as a function of etiology. *Amer J Ment Defic, 57*: 484-494, 1953.
8. Gallagher, J. J.: *The Tutoring of Brain Injured Mentally Retarded Children*. Springfield, Thomas, 1960.
9. Hermelin, Beate, and O'Connor, N.: Effects of sensory input and sensory dominance on severely disturbed, autistic children and on subnormal controls. *Brit J Psychol, 55*:201-06, 1964.

10. Strauss, A. A., and Lehtinen, Laura: *Psychopathology and Education of the Brain Injured Child.* New York, Grune, 1947.
11. Strauss, A. A., and Kephart, N. C.: *Psychopathology and Education of the Brain Injured Child. Vol. 2, Progress in Theory and Clinic.* New York, Grune, 1955.

PART ONE
EVALUATION

I

DISORDERS OF ORAL COMMUNICATION

Edward D. Mysak

THIS CHAPTER IS CONCERNED with the factor of oral communication and its disorders in the education of CNS-impaired children. Broadly, the chapter will include a discussion of the effects of CNS involvement on oral communication and the educational process with a description of practical suggestions for the teacher on the use and improvement of oral communication in the classroom.

Cerebral dysfunction in this chapter refers to those conditions which have been variously described in the literature as "minimal brain damage,"[5] "minimal chronic brain syndromes,"[12] "brain injury."[16,17] Descriptions of this type of cerebral handicap follow.

Paine[12] has written,

> . . . Yet if one acknowledges that there are four main areas in which function may be deranged by a chronic brain lesion (motor, intellectual, perceptual, convulsive), it is plausible that there should exist subclinical affections in each area. It is submitted that patients with, for example, overt motor disabilities may show minimal involvement in other areas; and that other patients may show only subclinical or borderline involvement in any area, but usually in more than one.

Hagberg[5] in reporting on his study of twenty-six apparently normal children and young adults indicated,

> . . . As a whole, this group of apparently normal children known to have had early disorders of the brain and showing a high incidence of minor sequelae of different types illustrates the common practical problems of "minimal brain damage" . . . . It is important to emphasize that a high proportion of these slightly damaged children do have a handicap, although it is often so well hidden that their difficulties in daily life are misunderstood by parents, teachers, doctors, and even the patients themselves.

Related to the orientation of the present chapter is Denhoff and Robinault's[2] recent definition of "cerebral palsy," They say that it

. . . may be defined as one component of a group of childhood neurologic disorders which reflect cerebral dysfunction rather than damage per se and which may result from cerebral maldevelopment, infection, injury, or anoxia before or during birth or in the early years of life. Delayed maturation or even intense emotional stress can also be causative.

They include in these pediatric neurologic disabilities, the syndromes of cerebral palsy, mental retardation, epilepsy, hyperkinetic behavior disorder, and even childhood schizophrenia. The authors refer to these conditions collectively as the "syndromes of cerebral dysfunction." "Affected children may demonstrate a variety of neuromotor, intellectual, sensory, and behavioral findings singly or in combinations and varying in degree." Accordingly, this latter statement, concerning the symptoms of children with cerebral dysfunction, applies to the minimally brain-damaged child as well.

Twitchell and Ehrenreich[18] have reported recently on the presence of exaggerated avoiding responses of the foot as subtle changes which ". . . may be the only abnormalities detected on routine neurological examination in children with 'mental deficiency' or a minimal 'brain-damage syndrome'."

Strauss and Kephart[16] have stated, "We must therefore expand our concept of brain injury to include children with 'normal' I.Q.'s." Relative to brain malformations, they point out

. . . Obviously there must be all types of these malformations varying from the very gross and obvious . . . to extremely minor difficulties which can be detected only with the most refined technics and in many cases can be detected only by an observation of the resulting functional disorders in the organism.[16]

Finally, Myklebust,[10] in discussing children with aphasia, states:

. . . Presumably the central nervous system involvement is not limited to language capacity, but characteristically includes other functions. This is logical in view of the generalized organismic disturbance typically found in aphasic children. A disturbance of motor coordination can be considered as characteristic of the aphasic child. This motor disturbance can be described as mildly diffuse in-coordination, inferior grasp, and awkwardness rather than as obvious disabledness or cerebral palsy.

Despite the orientation of the chapter toward the "minimal brain-damage syndrome," it should be realized that, because of the organismic nature of CNS involvements, any affected individual may show varying degrees and combinations of sensory, perceptual, associative, motor, and behavioral symptoms; and, in that sense, much of the discussion will not necessarily be limited to any one type or severity of neurologic disorder.

Of main importance to the goal of the present chapter is the fact that children with CNS problems usually have disturbances in oral communication which, in turn, contribute to learning difficulties in the classroom. Therefore, in the last analysis, the important consideration will be whether or not a particular cerebrally handicapped child, regardless of type or degree of CNS involvement, also has an oral-communication disorder which may be contributing to classroom difficulties — and, if so, what the classroom teacher can do about it.

ORAL COMMUNICATION AND THE EDUCATIONAL PROCESS

Before considering the effects of cerebral dysfunction on oral communication and the educational process, it would be well to review some of the obvious connections between oral communication, and teaching and learning.

Oral communication and educational processes are so interrelated and interdependent that the connections are usually taken for granted and, therefore, are rarely analyzed. When all things are equal, with respect to the children in a class, such an analysis is relatively unnecessary; however, when the children in the class have CNS disturbances, such an analysis may be important.

Transmission and Reception

To state the obvious, a prime function of the teacher is to transmit to the children in her class certain information about current events, geography, arithmetic, spelling, and so forth. Granted that the teacher may utilize objects, pictures, and written symbols as visual aids in this process of transmission of information, it should be remembered that most often her basic means, especially with young children, is via the use of oral symbols or oral teaching.

Since oral communication is so important in teaching and learning, and since CNS-involved children may have various types of oral-communicative disorders, the teacher must always be alert to the need to differentiate between (1) a learning disability and a problem in receiving and comprehending oral symbols, and (2) a learning disability and a problem in formulating and expressing oral symbols. In other words, the teacher may evaluate inappropriate verbal responses as a sign of poor learning or poor motivation when in actuality they may be reflections, at least in part, of primary problems in oral communication.

Oral Symbols and Thinking

There apparently is a substantial correlation between the development and use of oral symbols and thinking ability. Intellectual development depends a great deal on the ability of the child to represent the objects, acts, qualities, and relationships of the external world with symbols — basically verbal symbols. Symbols allow the child to manipulate external reality in his mind, and hence to solve problems on a mental rather than on an actual trial and error basis. Therefore, there appears to be a reciprocal and positive relationship between perceptual-conceptual development and oral-symbolic development.

Again, because the CNS-disturbed child may have specific problems in the area of oral-symbolic behavior, this difficulty may affect his learning processes. On the other hand, there is the implication that if a teacher could stimulate and expand oral language development in certain children, learning processes could be facilitated.

CEREBRAL DYSFUNCTION AND LEARNING

Sensory-Perceptual

The results of cerebral dysfunction which more directly involve learning processes are those associated with impaired sensory-perceptual functioning. It should also be understood that various types of motor deficits and experiential deprivations will also contribute to learning problems.

EXPERIENTIAL DEFICITS

As stated, certain primary sensory and motor problems will reduce the number of meaningful experiences that will be appreciated by the affected child and, hence, interfere with learning. In addition, however, secondary experiential deficits may be encountered because such a child is often difficult to manage and, consequently, (1) he may not be allowed to play with as many things, (2) he may not be taken to as many places, and (3) he may not have as many interpersonal relationships as the normal child. This reduction in the number of meaningful experiences, of course, may contribute to general learning as well as to language learning problems.

SENSORY

Visual and auditory acuity losses may be significant factors to consider when evaluating the brain-damaged child. Since the acquisition of symbolic behavior basically depends on the adequate functioning of the audio-visual sensory channels, which are so often involved in the affected child, special consideration must be given to the assessment of these sensory capacities.

PERCEPTUAL CAPACITY

Higher order receptive functioning such as that used in percept formation is also commonly involved in the brain-damaged individual. The child may show difficulty in organizing and structuring sensory input and, hence, may develop distorted and inaccurate perceptions.

Perceptual-Behavioral Manifestations

There are particular perceptual-behavioral symptoms which may be related to acquired or congenital CNS disturbances and which may also have an important bearing on general learning as well as language learning capacities. Some of the symptoms presented below have been discussed by various authorities with reference to brain-damaged adults; however, it is believed that these symptoms may also apply to children with congenital or developmental CNS involvements as well.

RISE AND LABILITY OF THRESHOLD

Goldstein[4] states that damage to the cortex causes a rise of threshold and a retardation of excitation for stimuli. The individual's receptive or perceptive capacity is reduced, and it takes longer for the damaged organism to react; for example, ". . . understanding may be disturbed if one speaks too quickly to such an individual." Therefore, giving brain-injured individuals more time to respond may be important to them. Increasing the duration of the stimulus, however, may not always bring improvement in perception either, because of the tendency of the involved individual toward lability of threshold. For example, a brain-injured person "may perceive if the visual stimulus is strong enough, but after a time he may cease to see the object in spite of continued stimulation."

PERSEVERATION

Another peculiarity of the brain-damaged individual, according to Goldstein,[4] is that when excitation does take place despite the raised threshold, it may "spread abnormally and last an unusually long time." A verbal response to a request, for example, may persist and be repeated many times in reaction to other requests. Berry and Eisenson[1] regard perseveration as a ". . . tendency for a specific act of behavior, an attitude, or a 'set' (mental or physical) to continue in operation when it is no longer appropriate to the situation at hand." They believe the tendency is most likely to manifest itself when the individual finds situations too difficult, or when situations change rapidly.

Strauss and Lehtinen[17] recognize two forms of perseveration: the first is known as repetitive perseveration and is characterized by the repetition of the same response several times; the second is known as iterative perseveration (delayed perseveration) and is characterized by the repetition of a response given two or more responses earlier.

DISTRACTIBILITY

Goldstein[4] believes that external stimuli acquire an exaggerated importance for brain-damaged individuals due to the loss in the individual's ability to retain previous experiences and associate them with external stimuli; therefore, the external stimuli remain new, different and distracting. Berry and Eisenson[1] view this condition as a disturbance of attention which is ". . . a state in which the individual becomes set to select and respond to a specific pattern of stimuli or to one situation to the exclusion of others." They state further that ". . . even with the increase of effort, non-relevant stimuli may successfully compete with relevant ones. Responses may be made which, on an intellectual basis at least, the patient would prefer not to make."[1]

FIXATION

The other side of distractibility is periodic behavioral fixation; this type of "freeze" behavior may often be seen in the CNS-impaired child. Here the child may be observed to fixate on some activity, and the teacher may find it difficult to shift his attention. As in other examples of disequilibrium in the nervous system, the mechanism which responds particularly quickly and intensely may also respond inappropriately, and apparent excitation (distractibility activity) may rapidly become apparent inhibition (fixation activity).

DISINHIBITION

Myklebust[10] describes distractibility as forced responsiveness to stimuli from without, while disinhibition is characterized by an inability to control distractions from within. Postponing, or awaiting expected occurrences may be extremely difficult for brain-damaged children who tend to react reflexively and immediately to internal motivations and urges. For example, a statement from the teacher such as, "We will play with the blocks in about five minutes," may be an especially difficult one for the brain-damaged child to abide by.

OVER-RESPONSE

Strauss and Kephart[16] have said that the brain-injured child's ". . . activities are characterized by great intensity and a great expenditure of energy." He expends more energy than is normal in accomplishing something. This is due, they believe, to the fact that the affected child ". . . does not drain off as much energy in non-overt activity, and he has a higher level of energy since less is drained off through ordinary response channels." It should be appreciated that over-response behavior may especially interfere with those classroom learning situations which require small muscle activity.

FIGURE-GROUND DISTURBANCES

Distinguishing between foreground and background during the act of perception is obviously very important. For example, in order to efficiently perceive certain objects in a picture, one must selectively ignore the background stimuli and focus on the desired primary stimulus. Similarly, efficient auditory perception of speech requires that the listener focus on the voice of the speaker and disregard the background noise. Goldstein[4] states that ". . . In normal performances the figure and ground processes are in a definite relation." In the individual with cortical damage this figure-ground relation may be disturbed. He states further that the brain-damaged individual will many times actually invert figure and ground situations so that he may, for example, answer *yes* when he means *no* or *black* when he means *white*.

ABSTRACT ATTITUDE

Goldstein[4] has described another symptom of the brain-injured as the loss of the ability to abstract. The individual responds only to immediate experiences, objects or situations; he finds it difficult to transcend immediate sense impressions and to consider situations from a conceptual point of view. Berry and Eisenson[1] have included in their definition that the brain-injured child experiences difficulties in acts such as pretending, seeing that certain elements belong together, analyzing a whole into parts and then, in turn, synthesizing elements into the essential whole, and in generalizing behavior.

MEMORY

Memory is another faculty which is found greatly reduced or limited in the brain-injured individual. Berry and Eisenson[1] state that "Memory may be weakened for immediate situations because of a primary defect of attention." Another reason for defective retention is the weakened ability of the brain-injured to verbalize, and, therefore, the facts that are attainable through attention cannot be easily recorded. Normal persons retain those experiences which they can most easily verbalize.

RIGIDITY

Rigidity and orderliness are other characteristics found among affected individuals. Goldstein[4] indicates that these traits provide a way of keeping the physical world under control and permit operation with a minimum of effort. It should be readily apparent that behavioral rigidity is directly opposed to learning, which implies exposure to, and integration of, new experiences.

CATASTROPHIC RESPONSE

This type of response may take place if the affected individual is confronted with a task which is too difficult. If he cannot avoid the situation he may respond catastrophically; that is, he may exhibit "vascular changes, irritability, evasiveness or aggressiveness." He may even resort to motor or sensory losses, or in extreme cases he may lose consciousness completely.[1] Goldstein[4] indicates that it is a response of the whole organism in a situation where a successful performance does not seem possible. Such a tendency would be especially detrimental to the child who is involved with learning a complicated task.

WITHDRAWAL

When withdrawal tendencies are observed, they may be interpreted as attempts by the affected individual to avoid conflict or difficulty.[1] He desires to be away from people who make demands. He wants to avoid new situations and in this way reduce frustration. Again, this tendency is detrimental to learning since classroom activities are so frequently new, demanding, and stimulating.

In summary, the purpose of this discussion of organic behavioral manifestations is to bring symptoms to the attention of the teacher so that he may be able to recognize them, and to encourage the teacher to consider ways and means of preventing or counteracting these debilitating behavior patterns when they do occur.

CEREBRAL DYSFUNCTION AND ORAL-COMMUNICATIVE DISORDERS

CNS involvement may disturb auditory functioning, speech, sound maturation, and oral-symbolic development.

Audition may be deficient in many respects in the brain-damaged child. There may be acuity losses because of pathology in the peripheral mechanism of hearing, as well as auditory-perceptual disturbances such as figure-ground discrimination and memory span difficulties. In addition, there may also be various secondary auditory problems. For example, when actual auditory problems exist and these are not detected or properly treated, the child may eventually find it unrewarding to attend auditorially, and he may begin to use less of his auditory capacity. Consequently, a type of "auditory atrophy" may manifest itself. Further, because of his problems, the involved child may be exposed to many unpleasant auditory experiences such as verbal criticism, punishment, and so forth, and he may eventually begin to reject auditory events. All of these auditory difficulties have a bearing on general learning and language learning ability.

CNS impairment may also affect the movements of the mandible, lips, tongue, velum and pharynx and, consequently, may interfere with the child's ability to articulate adequately. These difficulties may be so great as to be readily apparent, or so subtle as to be detected only after careful examination.

For the classroom teacher, possibly the most important aspect of the child's oral-communicative problem may be his difficulty in the use of oral-linguistic symbols. Part of such a disturbance will stem from the auditory and peripheral speech-mechanism deficits just described; however, much of the difficulty may arise from primary disorders in the learning, formulating, receiving and expressing of oral symbols.

Reports in the Literature

Various descriptions of the oral-communicative functioning of the minimally brain-damaged child may be found in the literature. It should be of value at this point to organize and to discuss some of the observations that have been made.

LANGUAGE DEVELOPMENT

Strauss and Kephart[16] recognize that brain-injured children frequently show "a definite retardation or marked lack of language behavior." They believe that the condition is different in many respects from aphasic difficulties in adults, and hence they

. . . prefer to use the term oligophasia for the conditions found in children and to mean by this term a deficit of language or lack of its development. Language is here defined as "a symbolic expression of thought," excluding in this definition disturbances of the speech organs proper as well as disturbances of hearing.

They define three types of oligophasia.

. . . Receptive oligophasia is primarily a disturbance in auditory perception so that foreground and background relations of auditory elements cannot be clearly recognized. Expressive oligophasia is a disturbance in the process of recognizing and forming phonemic patterns and their transference to the executive organs of speech. Central oligophasia is a disorder of symbolization, due to imperfection of auditory-perceptual, or other perceptual and sensory-motor schemata, so that a symbolic schemata of language cannot be clearly evolved.[16]

Ingram[6] spoke of the need to differentiate between acquired dysphasia, dyslexia, and dysgraphia in childhood from developmental dysphasia, dyslexia, and dysgraphia. He indicated there is strong evidence which suggests that the specific developmental disorders are genetically determined. In describing the various symptoms of specific developmental dysphasia, Ingram revealed that the ". . . more severely affected patients are slow in acquiring words and in making phrases."

AUDITORY PERCEPTION

Relative to auditory-perceptual ability, Lewis, Strauss, and Lehtinen[8] described the brain-injured child as one whose ". . . perception and organization of auditory stimuli are poor. He confuses speech sounds which are similar, or he may reverse syllables within a word such as *emeny* for *enemy*. The damage is often so mild that the child may be without a very obvious speech defect."

Again, in Ingram's[6] description of the various symptoms in children with developmental dysphasia he stated that

> . . . They tend to make mistakes in arranging the component syllables to make meaningful words, omitting some, replacing others by inappropriate speech sounds (especially those which sound similar), and reversing and otherwise confusing their order . . . Neologisms are frequent . . .

He also revealed that a significant portion of patients with

> . . . retarded language development, also suffer from impaired ability to comprehend speech, especially in their early years . . . Even when some comprehension of speech has developed it is often imperfect, and many patients acquire the habit of asking automatically for whatever is said to them to be repeated . . . Patients with severe degrees of "word deafness" often rely very greatly on lip-reading and on gesture to perceive the meaning of what is said to them . . . .

ARTICULATION

Paine,[12] in his support of the concept of a syndrome of minimal brain damage, described forty-one children who were referred for neurological consultation because of poor school work, overactivity, or nervousness and emotional problems. Even though none of the children had previously been diagnosed definitely as having any neurological abnormalities, "Thirty-one of these children showed definite abnormal neurological signs, and nine of the other ten were at least excessively clumsy." With reference to speech, Paine indicated that, "Speech was normal in about half the patients, but nine showed varying degrees of dysarthria, slowing, slurring, or dysarticulation. . . ."

Again Ingram,[6] in speaking of children with developmental dysphasia, said they are

. . . slow in the acquisition of speech sounds; they show retarded articulatory development . . . defective pronunciation of consonants is usually inconstant. Consonants are more often incorrectly pronounced when they occur at the end of words than at the beginning. They are more often incorrectly articulated if they occur in clusters, or are repeated in single or in contiguous words, than when they are single . . . abnormalities of pronunciation are commonly associated with irregularities of rhythm and abnormalities of stress and intonation . . . .

GRAMMAR

Strauss and Kephart,[16] in describing the speech problems of brain-injured children, reported that ". . . Agrammatism is common, and grammatical confusions are prevalent, even among children from environmental situations where good grammar is habitually used. Thus one child, in describing a game of tag said, 'One boy they are it.' The same child said, 'I went to school across from the street'."

In Ingram's[6] description of the speech of children with developmental dysphasia he also remarked that ". . . Small words, especially those with only syntactical significance, are often omitted or mistaken. . . . Grammar, sentence-structure, and the ability to express complex ideas by an organized sequence of sentences are all impaired."

SEMANTICS

There have been many reports of brain-damaged children frequently revealing a lack of meaning associated with their verbalization.

Strauss and Kephart[16] have said,

We have seen that the brain-injured child has particular difficulty in those aspects of perception which require the organization of elements into wholes or combinations of elements into manageable units. It would therefore be expected that he would have more than average difficulty in developing language as a symbolism since this type of development rests almost entirely upon combining elements and organizing various factors of many situations into one unitary concept. We would expect that this child would frequently show a paucity of meaning attached to a given word. In like manner we would expect his meanings to vary from time to time as now one phase and then another of his incomplete concepts assumes primary importance. That is, in fact, the type of language behavior which we often observe in brain-injured children.

They go on to say,

> The vocabulary of the brain-injured child has frequently been shown to be as great as that of a normal child of the same age. He knows a large number of words. He has difficulty, however, in combining these words, in changing their meaning in subtle ways to suit the requirements of his present expression. So, although from the point of view of vocabulary he may be superior, he runs into trouble when he uses the words which he has.[16]

Lewis, Strauss, and Lehtinen[8] have reported of the brain-injured child's tendency toward "wayward associations."

> . . . For example, in reading about a dog, the child may be impelled to think of Rin-Tin-Tin, the Wonder Dog, and asks "What is a wonder?" Or, the sound of the verb, "does," triggers the association of "Duz, a miracle for clothes," and he asks, "What is a miracle?"

The authors also report that inadequate use of language sometimes results "in apparent irrelevancies."[8] As an example, they state that a child may say she saw the sun shining even though she may have only seen a small amount of light coming through the clouds on a cloudy day. They also described the tendency for adolescent brain-injured boys "to use profane or visceral words indiscriminately."[8] Finally, they report:

> It is not unusual to find that some brain-injured children are highly verbal. They seem to have good expressive language facility but some of this verbal facility may be imitative. The child may use words without being certain of their content. The percepts or concepts which the words represent may not be firmly evolved . . . . In highly verbal brain-injured children, there is often a gap between the apparent ability to use language and its comprehension.
>
> There may also be a wide discrepancy between talking and doing. The child's actual performance may be on a lower level than his ability to talk about it.[8]

Hagberg,[5] in describing another group of apparently "normal" children with minimal brain damage resulting from spontaneously arrested hydrocephalus, revealed that three showed a behavior-type often seen in cases with a more pronounced hydrocephalus which he and his colleagues have called "the cocktail party syndrome." "These children are very sociable and pseudo-bright and love to chatter but usually do not know very much what they are talking about."

Finally Ingram,[6] in speaking of his dysphasic group, said that ". . . affected children also tend to fail to find the words they want. Either speech becomes arrested, or they produce equivalent circumlocutionary phrases instead. At other times an inappropriate word is uttered, frequently one with similar sounds or associations to the word which the child really wanted."

Report of a Study

Some additional information on CNS disturbance and oral-linguistic functioning is provided in the findings of a recent doctoral investigation.

Reichstein[14] administered the Illinois Test of Psycholinguistic Abilities[7] to a group of peripherally deaf children (apparently without CNS involvement) and to a group of aphasic children (predominantly of the receptive variety and apparently with CNS involvement). The results indicated that the non-brain-damaged-deaf group was superior to the aphasic group in some linguistic abilities: (1) vocal encoding (child shown series of familiar objects and asked to verbalize about them), (2) auditory-vocal association (sentence completion type test, e.g., "Father is big, baby is ————."), (3) auditory decoding (*yes* or *no* responses to to such questions as, "Do bicycles drink?"), (4) auditory-vocal sequencing (digit repetition test), (5) auditory-vocal automatic responses (assessed by a grammar test, e.g., child is shown a picture of a hat and a picture of two hats and the examiner says, "Here is a hat." "Here are two ————." The child completes the sentence.)

In short, the findings indicate that minimally brain-damaged children are significantly inferior to non-brain-injured children in such verbal activities as: vocal encoding, auditory-vocal association, auditory decoding, auditory-vocal sequencing, and auditory-vocal automatic responses. These findings might be considered during oral teaching and oral language stimulation activities.

Review of Case Reports

The following data are presented for the purpose of providing additional clinical information on the oral-communicative involvements of brain-damaged children. Also they offer further support of the information reported in the literature.

The present writer examined the records of all children referred to him for speech and hearing evaluations during a three-year period and found fifteen that could be put in the category of minimal brain damage. The material below represents data obtained from the initial examinations of these fifteen children.

There were ten boys who ranged from three to thirteen years of age, and five girls who ranged from three to eight years of age. The information will be divided into history and examination data; further, only data which were considered relevant to this chapter have been included.

HISTORY

Prenatal histories included one child born of a mother with Rh negative blood, one whose mother reported coordination problems in the family, one whose obese mother had to lose one-hundred pounds before she was able to conceive and who suffered from fainting spells and chest pains during the last trimester, and one whose mother reported "spotting" during the fourth to the seventh months of pregnancy. Natal histories included one late delivery, one case of cyanosis immediately following birth, one cesarean section delivery, one with some type of umbilical cord difficulty at birth, one premature delivery, one breech delivery, one precipitate delivery in conjunction with delayed respiration, and one was the product of a triplet delivery and was considerably underweight. Motor developmental histories included the following: five with some degree of slowness in learning to walk and ten who walked within, or at the outside limits of normalcy. Medical histories included one child with "head banging" until five years, one with some form of seizure involvement, one with a head concussion at one year, three with enuresis and one who had surgery to correct strabismus.

EXAMINATIONS

The following are reports of some of the data, usually acquired by the writer when he conducted general speech and hearing evaluations. Four items will be specifically discussed.

Peripheral Speech Mechanism. Two measures were usually made here: one involved performances on nonverbal activities of the articulators (mandible, lips, tongue, velum) such as opening, closing, protruding and elevating activities, and the other involved performances on verbal activities such as producing "puh," "tuh," and "kuh" as quickly as possible (articulatory diadochocinesia). The results were that three showed abnormal velar activity, four showed normal nonverbal movements but abnormal verbal movements, three showed an excessive amount of involuntary movement of the tongue in the rest position, and two showed abnormal nonverbal and verbal movements of the articulators.

Hearing. Whenever possible, three types of auditory functioning were assessed. First, auditory acuity which refers to an individual's threshold responses for pure tones; second, auditory memory span for speech sounds, which refers to an individual's ability to perceive increasing numbers of vowels and consonants, retain these sounds, and then to revocalize them; and third, auditory discrimination which assesses the individual's ability to discriminate between various combinations of similar sounding syllables. The last two tests may be seen as tests for types of auditory-perceptual functioning. The results were that two showed rapid accommodation (decreasing, to loss of response to auditory stimuli) and inconsistency of response, two showed normal acuity but abnormal memory span, three showed normal acuity but abnormal memory span and discrimination, one showed normal acuity and discrimination but abnormal memory span, and two showed a mild reduction in acuity.

Speech Sound Development. Speech sound maturation is determined by conducting a phonetic analysis of the child's speech-sound ability. Sounds develop in a more or less consistent manner, and usually there is a certain progression from the simpler bilabial, or lip sounds (e.g., *B, P*) to the more complicated lingua-alveolar or tongue-tip sounds (e.g., *S, Z, SH*). These sounds are also studied in the various positions in which they may be found in a word — that is, at the beginning, middle, or end. The results revealed that thirteen showed various degrees of interference with speech-sound maturation, and only two showed near-normal speech-sound maturation.

Further, relative to speech production, three of the children exhibited excessive disfluency, and six demonstrated excessive nasality which was very likely related to velar-movement deficiencies.

Language. Evaluations were made of receptive and expressive oral-linguistic capacities. The findings were as follows: four showed both receptive and expressive deficits, five showed relatively intact receptive language with a substantial lack in expressive language, two showed near-normal receptive capacity with excessive agrammatisms during expression, and only three showed near-normal expressive and receptive oral language capacities. Some of the specific symptoms observed included excessive use of gesture, agrammatisms, verbal perseveration, inability to find desired words, and echolalia.

In summary, the review of the case reports of fifteen minimally brain-damaged children showed that a substantial number had prenatal and natal histories which suggest disposition to neuropathology. In addition, positive speech and hearing findings included velar movement deficits, involuntary tongue activity, deficiencies in verbal diadochocinesia, auditory-perceptual dysfunctioning, speech-sound-maturational problems, and various types of oral-linguistic anomalies.

ORAL LANGUAGE THEORY AND STIMULATION

Before offering specific suggestions for improving oral communication in a classroom, a discussion of oral language theory is considered in order.

Theories of Language Learning

Knowledge of at least two theories of language learning should prove valuable to the classroom teacher.

In a recent article by the present writer,[11] Mowrer's[9] Autism Theory of speech development was described in this way,

> . . . In essence, the theory indicates that certain sounds or word-noises may be elicited from a child by the following sequence of events: (a) A speaker comes to represent positive emotional connotations for the child by engaging in such pleasure-producing actions as feeding and playing. (b) A speaker produces a specific word-noise just before and as he confronts the child. (c) A speaker eventually evokes positive emotional feelings within the child by his word-noise alone. (d) The child experiences a concomitant positive emotional feedback when he approximates the speaker's word-noise during random vocalization. (e) The child repeats the approximation and strives to perfect it because he feels greater degrees of satisfaction from the feedback when he produces the word-noise more accurately. (f) The child retains the learned word-noise because of the influence of social approval.

A second theory of oral language development, described by Penfield,[13] has a neurophysiological orientation. The present writer[11] has described the theory in this way,

> He [Penfield] describes the formation in the CNS of three types of neuronal patterns which represent what he calls the conceptual, sound, and verbal units. For example, the word "milk" is acquired by the child in the following manner: (a) By experiencing milk many times and in many ways, he [the child] eventually establishes a neuronal pattern, or conceptual unit in the concept mechanism (both hemispheres involved) which represents the idea of milk. (b) By consistently hearing the word-noise "milk" in association with the experience, he eventually establishes a neuronal pattern, or sound unit, in the cortico-thalamic speech areas in the left hemisphere which represents the heard word-noise "milk." (c) By the frequent association of conceptual and sound units an automatic and reciprocal connection between the two units developed. (d) By virtue of forming conceptual and sound units and the reflexive connection between the two, he eventually establishes a neuronal pattern, or verbal unit, in the cortico-thalamic speech areas in the left hemisphere which represents the spoken word-noise "milk."

Organismic Development of Oral Language

In addition to familiarity with the above theories, it is believed that a comparatively complete description of the normal sequential development of oral language should contribute further ideas to the teacher who is interested in helping her CNS-disturbed children in oral communication.

The following outline of language development is based on a recent article by the present writer,[11] and it will emphasize the interrelatedness of the general motor, perceptual, and vocalization mechanisms in the development of oral language. It is believed that before a particular child develops efficient, meaningful oral symbols, there is a simultaneous maturation of his perceptorium (basically visual, auditory, and tactile receptors). This maturation enables him to experience the environment and to develop the necessary percepts — his motor system conveys his receptors and brings them in contact with the various aspects of the environment for the purpose of developing these percepts, and his vocalization mechanism allows him to code his percepts with appropriate oral symbols. No description of oral language development is really complete unless these three types of maturation are discussed in relation to one another at all of the various stages of oral language development; it should be apparent that this particular view of oral language development has special pertinence to the child with minimal brain injury since he may show varying degrees of involvement in any or all of these areas. Accordingly, then, oral language development will be discussed in connection with the concomitant perceptual and general motor system maturations at each successive stage of oral language development. There will be no attempt to give detailed accounts of perceptual and motor system developments, but rather the more outstanding aspects of each type of maturation will be mentioned. Further, the writer wants to acknowledge that information on motor, perceptual, and language-developmental progressions has been drawn from many sources.[1,3,10,15,16]

Oral language development will be divided into two stages — the *pre-propositional stage* and the *propositional stage*. Time schedules should be viewed in terms of approximations rather than as absolutes.

PRE-PROPOSITIONAL STAGE

During the pre-propositional stage, the child's utterances are not recognizable as word forms; this period encompasses approximately the first twelve months of life.

Perceptually, the child's visual processes develop from (1) just beginning to watch his mother's face when she feeds or talks to him at one month, (2) to quickly fixating within six to twelve inches, on small objects such as toys, and reaching for them at six months, (3) to watching with interest the movements of people, animals, and cars at twelve months. Auditorially, the child may (1) startle in response to unexpected loud sounds, or may immobilize to the ringing of a bell at one month, (2) turn to the source of the sound, such as a rattle or mother's voice, at six months, and (3) respond to the calling of his name at twelve months. Hand and tactual activity show (1) bilateral reaching and grasping activity at six months, and (2) neat pincer-grasping at twelve months.

Motorially, the child has advanced from rolling over, holding the head erect in the supine position, and reaching at six months; to pulling himself to the standing position at twelve months.

During the course of this perceptual and motor development, the child has produced (1) reflexive vocalization (crying, screaming, gutteral noises) during the first month without any apparent appreciation of his vocalization, (2) babbling or the using of single syllables such as "muh," "buh," "guh" up to six months, with self-appreciation of this vocalization being shown by the child's facial expressions or by his making of the sounds during pleasant moments, (3) lalling, or the repeating of self-produced sounds or sound combinations (auditory feedback) such as, ma-ma, da-da, la-la up to ten months, and (4) echolalia, or the imitating of sounds and sound combinations made by others, up to twelve months.

PROPOSITIONAL

From twelve to eighteen months (during which time the normal child learns to walk) the first recognizable words appears, and by eighteen months the child may use as many as twenty words.

From this initial use of propositional or meaningful words, to about three years, there is a rapid increase in percept formation and in words to code these percepts. By three years of age, the child may give his full name and use about two hundred words. An interesting aspect of this development is that the child may be seen talking to himself rather continually while playing (gestures, mimicry and expressions are used as much as words at this time), and aside from expressing wants and needs, this appears to be a stage during which the child, with the aid of speech, clarifies, expands, categorizes, and maintains an organized sequence to his perceptualization. From about three to five years, the process of mature intercommunication begins to emerge. The child will describe recent events and experiences, and will listen to and tell long stories; in addition, the child will criticize, request, threaten, and ask questions. From about five years to seven or eight years, there is further perceptual refinement, and percepts no longer are limited to a representation of the object experienced; in turn, words no longer merely represent objects but are symbols for differentiated perceptions. As symbolization develops, the child analyzes and synthesizes elements from a number of perceptions into new wholes or conceptual units. It is at this time that the child's language resembles adult symbolic intercommunication.

In conclusion, the following four principles with respect to the learning of *oral language* may be derived from this study of oral language theory.

The "Good Sound" Orientation. The teacher might find it advantageous if she comes to represent a positive and pleasant experience for her children. She should speak a great deal while the children are experiencing pleasant moments and as little as possible during unpleasant moments such as during periods of verbal discipline.

The Need For Perceptual Clarification. The general importance of aiding CNS-disturbed children with percept formation is recognized, and now the specific importance of an adequate percept unit to the development of adequate sound and verbal units should also be appreciated. Relative to clarifying visual percepts, manipulation of size, form, and the use of texture and color should all be kept in mind. Auditory-percept accentuation may be accomplished by manipulating loudness, pitch, quality and duration factors, and by eliminating background noises. The use of materials that will stimulate more than one sensory channel (synesthesia) should also be considered. For example, a real apple provides visual, tactile, olfactory and gustatory stimulation; a picture of an apple merely offers visual stimulation.

The Primacy of Oral Language Reception. Since children comprehend gestures and tonal aspects of vocalization and sound units before they use verbal units, time might be well-spent in playing receptive stimulation games. For example, the use of gestures alone, words alone, or a combination of gestures and words might be incorporated into various verbal games (e.g., "give it to me" games [11 mo.], simple commands [16 mo.], point to body parts and to objects in pictures [18 mo.]). This provides the necessary receptive stimulation and also periodically allows for simpler, more easily accomplished expression in the form of whole body responses.

The Primacy of Intracommunication Behavior. It may be recalled that in the pre-propositional as well as propositional stages of oral language development, intrapersonal vocalization initially predominates over interpersonal vocalization. During the propositional stage of oral language development, for example, much of the child's oral-symbol behavior apparently represents vocalizations of his perceptual processes. The teacher might encourage such verbalization by reporting aloud on her movements as she engages in various class activities. "Speak-do" games can also be played with the children. Here they are encouraged to accompany their own activities with a running commentary or monologue. Accompanying gesture and pantomime may also be used.

Oral Language Stimulation

It should be understood that whenever possible, specific oral language stimulation work should be planned and conducted by qualified speech and hearing clinicians. Further, it should be considered appropriate for brain-injured children to receive complete speech and hearing evaluations so that proper attention might be given to any oral-communicative disorder which may require the services of the clinician.

The following represent specific techniques of oral-language stimulation which can be incorporated in the classroom situation.

LABELING

A teacher making personal contact with particular objects should name them aloud once or twice. She should also do the same when the children make contact with various objects. This aids the children in making desired perceptual-linguistic associations.

SENTENCE COMPLETION

Play the game of having the children finish sentences — for example, "When I am hungry, I ———."

DEFINITIONS

Have the children define various words; or reverse the procedure and have the children give the word which best represents a given description. Practice in the use of dictionaries could be made a part of this verbal game.

IMAGERY AND ASSOCIATION

The teacher might present an object and produce an appropriate, accompanying word. After a pause, the children may be asked to *listen* once more for the word but this time in their imaginations or mind's ears. The procedure may also be reversed by removing the stimulus and repeating the word, and asking the children to *see* the object in their mind's eyes. When appropriate, they may be asked to *feel, smell,* or *taste* in their imaginations as well.

SOCIODRAMAS

This technique consists of re-creating certain familiar situations — such as at home, in the store, and so forth — and having the children improvise the dialogue. The teacher should initiate the verbalization and periodically inject verbalization in order to maintain the speaking situation.

ANALYSIS AND SYNTHESIS

An example of this technique is as follows: the teacher may name an object, for example, *chair,* and the child may be asked to analyze the object by naming its parts — for example, legs, back, seat; or the teacher may request a "build-up" (synthesis) rather than a "breakdown" of the idea of chair, and the child may be asked to name related pieces of furniture such as table and bureau.

"LOOK-DO-SPEAK"

To play this verbal game, large "action pictures" are presented, for example, a mother is shown holding a baby in her arms; the child is asked to mimic all movements and speech sounds that the picture may suggest.

AUDITORY DISCRIMINATION, MEMORY SPAN, ANALYSIS AND SYNTHESIS

Auditory-perceptual exercises might include having the children practice hearing the differences between similar sounding words, having them attempt to repeat longer words, phrases, and sentences, and having them break down words into syllables, or build up words from syllables.

ANTONYM-SYNONYM

This verbal game consists simply of practice in finding antonyms and synonyms.

WORD ASSOCIATION

This verbal exercise consists of having the child say the first word or words that come to mind after hearing the stimulus or lead word.

STORY CONTINUATION

Here the teacher has the children continue stories begun by the teacher or by another child. Each individual tells as much of the story as he wishes and passes the story to the next individual who must continue the story from that point.

FACILITATION OF COMMUNICATION DURING ORAL TEACHING

The final section of the chapter will offer ways for improving oral communication between the teacher and the children during more formal classroom situations; it will be divided into two parts — *speech production considerations* and *speech content considerations.*

Speech Production

In considering speech production factors, the emphasis is on preparing the environment and the children for the reception of the teacher's oral messages.

AUDITORY BACKGROUND

Because of the commonly found auditory-perceptual disturbances in these children, especially of the figure-ground variety, the classroom should be as free as possible of distracting background noises. Reducing distracting visual stimuli at the time of oral teaching by special lighting arrangements which accentuate the teacher's body and face might also be considered. Experimenting with soft background music to mask undesirable environmental noises might be attempted, too.

ATTENTION

To insure that the children are "tuned in," the teacher must develop some technique which attracts the children's eyes and ears toward her before she sends her oral messages. Tapping, the calling of the names of a few children, the holding up of a certain picture or sign, and the sounding of a specific buzzer or bell might all be tried with the purpose of making sure that the children are in a state of readiness for oral language reception.

SPEECH

The teacher should also experiment with varying the loudness, pitch, and quality of her voice. She may find that some children receive louder, higher-pitched voices better, or that some do better with soft, lower-pitched voices. Further, because of the auditory-perceptual factor, the teacher may find that some degree of over-articulation plus some reduction in the rate of speech might also be of assistance.

Speech Content

Once the appropriate auditory background has been achieved, the desired attention established, and the ideal voice, articulation and rate modes determined, the teacher should direct her attention to the most efficient manner of formulating her oral message.

WORDS

Whenever possible, the words used should be *concrete* rather than *abstract*. They should be words which may readily evoke images — apple, boy, run. Words which are similar in sound should be avoided in the same phrase or sentence — for example, "The boy has a toy." Because of auditory memory span difficulties, polysyllabic words should also be avoided.

SENTENCES

Sentences should be short, simple, direct and descriptive. Further, when an instruction consists of a series of ideas, the proper time sequence should be given, for example, "First, you do . . . then, . . . and, finally. . . ."

INTEGRATION

The teacher should always allow ample time for the integration of her oral messages. There should be longer than usual pauses after certain thought units have been expressed, to allow the children time to make proper associations. Having the child repeat certain requests or questions before he actually responds might also be tried. This latter step enables the teacher to know whether the message has been properly received, and it may also further assist the child in making the appropriate associations between words and ideas.

REPETITION, RESTRUCTURING, AND REDUNDANCY

When experiencing difficulty in communicating certain thoughts, most teachers will naturally try repeating the oral message. If this does not work, however, restructuring the sentence using simpler syntax and more concrete words might be attempted. Using telegrammatic-type sentence structure could also be tried. The principle of redundancy or saying the same thing in many ways, as well as "over-saying" it, is also to be kept in mind as a way of "getting through."

LINGUISTIC AIDS

While the teacher is speaking, picture, object, and gesture-pantomime support might be very important. That is, when a certain concept is to be taught, any objects or pictures that might reify the accompanying words should be gathered and utilized when needed. Liberal use of appropriate gestures, facial expressions, body postures is also recommended as a possible way of facilitating oral message integration. Onomatopoeic support might also be considered; that is, when describing certain animals or objects which produce characteristic sounds, these sounds might be made at the appropriate times.

CHILDREN'S RESPONSES

Oral responses from the children should also be evaluated carefully. Allow the children to use gestures and pantomime to help in their expression. They should also be allowed to use supportive objects, pictures, or drawings. When oral responses from a particular child are unclear, the teacher should feel free to verbalize restructured versions of the child's oral attempts so that the child may be given an opportunity to verify or correct the teacher's interpretation; further, this procedure allows the child to hear an acceptable oral expression of his thoughts.

REFERENCES

1. Berry, M. F., and Eisenson, J.: *Speech Disorders: Principles and Practices of Therapy*. New York, Appleton, 1956, pp. 391-395.
2. Denhoff, E., and Robinault, Isabel P.: *Cerebral Palsy and Related Disorders*. New York, McGraw, 1960, p. 25.
3. Gesell, A., and Amatruda, C. S.: *Developmental Diagnosis*. New York, Harper, 1948.
4. Goldstein, K.: *Language and Language Disturbances*. New York, Grune, 1948, pp. 4, 5, 12-14.

5. Hagberg, B.: The sequelae of spontaneously arrested infantile hydrocephalus. *Develop Med Child Neurol, 4:*583-87, 1962.

6. Ingram, T. T. S.: Pediatric aspects of specific developmental dysphasia, dyslexia and dysgraphia. *Cereb Palsy Bull, 2:*254-77, 1960.

7. Kirk, S. A., and McCarthy, J. J.: The Illinois test of psycholinguistic abilities — an approach to differential diagnosis. *Amer J Ment Defic, 66:*399-412, 1961.

8. Lewis, R. S.; Strauss, A. A., and Lehtinen, Laura E.: *The Other Child.* New York, Grune, 1960, pp. 53, 57, 60, 126, 130.

9. Mowrer, O. H.: Hearing and speaking: an analysis of language learning. *J Speech Hearing Dis, 23:*143-152, 1958.

10. Myklebust, H. R.: Aphasia in children — language development and language pathology, and diagnosis and training. In Travis, L. E. (Ed.) : *Handbook of Speech Pathology.* New York, Appleton, 1957, pp. 516, 525.

11. Mysak, E. D.: Organismic development of oral language. *J. Speech Hearing Dis, 26:*377-84, 1961.

12. Paine, R. S.: Minimal chronic brain syndromes in children. *Develop Med Child Neurol, 4:*21-7, 1962.

13. Penfield, W., and Roberts, L.: *Speech and Brain Mechanisms.* Princeton, Princeton, 1959.

14. Reichstein, J.: Auditory Threshold Consistency — A Basic Characteristic for Differential Diagnosis of Children with Communication Disorders. Unpublished Doctoral Dissertation, Teachers College, Columbia University, 1963.

15. Sheridan, Mary D.: *The Developmental Progress of Infants and Young Children.* London, Her Majesty's Stationery Office, 1960.

16. Strauss, A. A., and Kephart, N. C.: *Psychopathology and Education of the Brain-Injured Child.* Vol. 2, *Progress in Theory and Clinic.* New York, Grune, 1955, pp. 2, 37, 105, 106, 109, 110, 139.

17. Strauss, A., and Lehtinen, Laura: *Psychopathology and Education of the Brain-Injured Child.* New York, Grune, 1947, p. 51.

18. Twitchell, T. E., and Ehrenreich, D. L.: The plantar response in infantile cerebral palsy. *Devel Med Child Neurol, 4:*602-11, 1962.

II

HEARING IMPAIRMENT

ANNETTE R. ZANER

IN THE EARLY 1940's, spurred by research carried on during the Second World War, the field of audiology made rapid advances and the audiologist took his place among the professionals devoted to studying various aspects of human experience and behavior. The groups of subjects studied at that time consisted largely of the readily available populations in the armed forces. It was on adults, then, that the basic tests and measurements of hearing were developed. Most of these tests were designed to measure hearing in terms of auditory-sensitivity threshold levels across the wide band of frequencies normally audible to the human ear.

THE NATURE OF HEARING

There are three distinct anatomical divisions comprising the peripheral mechanism of hearing: the *outer ear,* through which sound travels by air conduction to the ear drum membrane (tympanic membrane), the *middle ear,* where airborne sound is converted into movements conducted by the structures of the middle ear to the oval window of the inner ear, and the *inner ear,* where the sound travels through the fluid of the inner ear (cochlea) to the hair cells of the VIII cranial nerve (auditory nerve) endings. Sound stimuli are then transmitted by the auditory nerve through the various neural centers to the cerebral cortex where they are perceived as meaningful sensations, and where, through presently unknown processes of association, the individual learns to differentiate sounds and to integrate various environmental sound patterns into a complex of symbol codes.

This ability to learn symbol codes of a solely auditory nature makes it possible for a person to function in a society where it is of supreme importance to know that the policeman's whistle means one thing and the fire engine siren another; that a tone of modified pitch means *alert* and a steady tone means *all clear;*

that one patterned rhythm of drum beats means *war* and another *peace;* and finally, that particular sequences of articulated speech sounds, when uttered in a universal pattern, become a *word* — a verbal symbol — which carries a particular meaning or thought.

Thus, the human ear receives sound stimuli from the environment and changes them into nerve impulses; the auditory nerve transmits these impulses to the higher neural centers; and the hearing and association areas of the brain integrate, associate, and interpret a variety of sounds at varying levels of loudness.

HEARING IMPAIRMENT

The term *hearing impairment,* when used in reference to adults, is described by the American Academy of Ophthalmology and Otolaryngology as ". . . the most general term for malfunction of the auditory mechanism." [2]*Hearing loss* is described as a more specific term, having acquired three distinct meanings: (1) impaired hearing sensitivity, as tested by either pure tones or speech, (2) the ratio, expressed in decibels, of the threshold of hearing of an ear at a specified frequency to a standard audiometric threshold, and (3) a change for the worse in an individual's threshold of hearing. In this chapter, however, the term *hearing loss* will be used interchangeably with *hearing impairment,* indicating auditory malfunction.

Hearing impairment can be *conductive* — that is, an impairment resulting from interference with the transmission of sound to the auditory nerve endings. Such an interference usually occurs in the outer or middle ear and, barring other complications, threshold levels measured by bone conduction are usually near normal. Hearing impairment can be *sensorineural* — that is, an impairment resulting from abnormality of the end organ, the auditory nerve trunk, or both.

For the purposes of this discussion, two classifications of hearing impairment will be considered: (1) impairment of hearing that appears to be *peripheral,* and (2) that which does not. Peripheral impairment usually reflects diminished auditory sensitivity, measured in terms of decibels, and it affects the individual's ability to *hear.* This type of impairment can refer to dysfunction of the end organ alone or dysfunction of the end organ and/or the auditory nerve.[33] Impairment which is not peripheral usually affects the individual's ability to *comprehend,* and it probably cannot be measured in terms of decibels. Non-peripheral impairment, according to some, implies dysfunction of the auditory cortex;[17] to others, it implies dysfunction of the auditory cortex and/or the auditory nerve. A combination of these two types of impairment is a relatively frequent finding.[15,22,37,39] There is much controversy among the authorities as to where, anatomically, one ends and the other begins. It is not the purpose here to debate these issues. Rather, the intention is to alert the reader to the existing controversies and their various implications.

THE MEASUREMENT OF HEARING

Adults

Pure tone audiometry is the most common means of testing hearing sensitivity. The sensitivity of an ear to pure tones is measured in two parameters, frequency and intensity. Using an audiometer, the ear is stimulated with a pure tone of a specific frequency. The intensity of this tone is gradually increased until the subject indicates that he hears the signal, usually by raising his hand; the tone is then gradually attenuated until a threshold level is ascertained. The procedure is repeated in each ear for all frequencies. Frequencies introduced in pure tone audiometry are fairly universal. The examiner is interested in testing at least those frequencies involved in speech. The degree of peripheral hearing impairment is expressed in decibels.

Other tests of sensitivity (as well as discrimination, intelligibility, and perception) fall under the heading of speech audiometry. With the wide variety of applicable tests and the different techniques available, the audiologist uses speech audiometry to test an individual's ability to hear speech signals (words, phrases, sentences) and to reproduce them accurately. The degree of hearing impairment for speech is expressed in decibels, and the ability to discriminate speech is expressed in percentage.

Pure tone audiometry has been widely criticized (by clinical audiologists as well as others) because it is *behavioral* audiometry, depending upon subjective responses. A number of different techniques have been developed recently in an attempt to objectify these responses. One such technique involves the use of psychogalvanic skin resistance (PGSR),[10] or electrodermal responses (EDR). Another technique involves the use of electroencephalic (EEG or EER) audiometry.[23]

Children

Frisina[21] has enumerated some of the problems surrounding examination of the hearing sensitivity of children.

1. Pure tone stimuli may be meaningless to some children.
2. Materials for speech audiometry are of little use with children who have delayed or defective language development.
3. Vocabulary used in speech audiometry was developed for adults and has not proved valid for children.
4. Children's limited linguistic skills impede communication of verbal instructions involving judgments of subtle differences.
5. Physical disabilities sometimes preclude standardized verbal or motor responses.
6. Speech anomalies often preclude scoring of oral responses.
7. Children sometimes refuse to accept earphones, precluding monaural measurements.
8. Children often refuse or are unable to cooperate in a general test situation.
9. The limited attention span in many children is problematic.
10. Some children are unable to associate stimulus with response.
11. Generalized immaturity in many children often sets limits on the accuracy of their judgments.
12. The fatigue factor in children requires more critical control than in adults.
13. Children may not be sufficiently interested in the procedures.

In an attempt to cope with these and other pertinent problems Myklebust[40] has stated the need to utilize informal as well as formal procedures when testing children. Formal procedures are defined as those that require active cooperation on the part of the subject (pure tone audiometry, tuning fork tests, and speech audiometry). Informal procedures are those which do not require active participation. In informal procedures, indirect responses are accepted as evidence of hearing.

Among the informal tests that Myklebust mentions, the *sound instrument* test is of interest. Ewing and Ewing[18,19] reported that stimulation with different sound instruments (bells, crickets, chimes) were found effective for different age groups. These instruments were evaluated for frequency range and intensity range so that response to stimulation could be meaningfully interpreted. Utley[47] further describes such techniques, emphasizing that a child younger than four or five is not necessarily too young to test. Other informal procedures include (1) observing and noting the child's response to sounds accidently produced during play (while playing with sound toys such as a squeaking doll, jack-in-the-box, quacking duck, or musical blocks he may unintentionally cause a sound to occur), and (2) observing and noting the child's response to imitations of his own vocalizations. All informal tests of hearing sensitivity in children are subject to interpretation of the child's reaction or responses by the examiner.

Myklebust reminds us that the formal tests of hearing were designed primarily for adults.[40] Numerous adaptations, modifications, and variations have been devised for administering pure tone audiometric tests to children, primarily to provide motivation for the child and to concretize his mode of responding. One kind of adaptation which has received much attention from audiologists is *play audiometry*. Play audiometry in its different forms [3,4,6,14,46,50] provides a play situation in which the child is taught to respond to a sound stimulus by performing a motor act (putting a peg in a board, throwing a block in a box). Hopefully, by making the activity meaningful, the child will participate in the game and respond reliably. Generally, these techniques have met with good success.[3,4]

Since an early report by Bordley *et al.,*[10] in 1948, electrophysiologic techniques have been utilized by a number of examiners for testing the hearing of children. The two different electrophysiologic techniques now in use and under continued investigation are EDR (or PGSR) audiometry[10] and EER (or EEG) audiometry.[23,49] In 1955, Barr[3,4] conducted a comparative study of EDR vs. play audiometry techniques in children under seven years of age. In eighty-five per cent of the cases tested, the two methods showed full agreement within accepted limits of clinical audiometry. Barr stated that since play audiometry is a pleasant experience in contrast to EDR or EER, it should be the preferred technique. However, with those children who do not learn to participate actively in the play tasks presented, this method sometimes cannot be used. In 1958, Withrow and Goldstein[49] showed that the validity of EER audiometry for testing young children has not as yet been demonstrated, nor are the techniques such that widespread clinical use is at this time feasible.

Suzuki[44,45] reports on recent experiences with the conditioned orientation reflex (COR) wherein an orientation reflex is excited by giving an acoustic as well as a visual stimulus simultaneously. This technique has proven useful for testing children between one and three.

There is broad agreement that the use of more than one test and the use of both formal and informal procedures in evaluating hearing sensitivity in children is essential.

HEARING IMPAIRMENT IN CHILDREN

Because of the intimate relationship between the ability to hear and the development of speech, children who do not begin to speak at the appropriate age are often suspected of having impaired hearing. DiCarlo[13] indicates that, prior to World War II, the failure in children to develop speech and language was frequently a critical criterion for determining hearing impairment. Today, the condition of delayed speech and language development is viewed as a communication impairment, one where a differential diagnosis may include one or more of the following etiological considerations: (1) mental retardation, (2) emotional disturbance, (3) impaired hearing sensitivity, and (4) impaired auditory reception, perception, integration and/or association.[34, 40,41,42] Mental retardation and emotional disturbance are discussed elsewhere in this text; thus, we may return to the discussion of impairment in *hearing* (peripheral) and impairment in *comprehension* (non-peripheral). It is of interest to the examiner and of potentially significant educational import for the disabled child that the audiologist attempt to differentiate between these disorders.

The differential diagnosis of auditory disorders in children is a topic that has been broadly studied in the past decade, widely reported on, and poorly understood. In the words of Bocca, ". . . we know a lot more about hearing but as little as ever about listening."[7] Clinical audiologists, speech and language pathologists, and neurophysiologists have attempted to identify differential diagnostic procedures by examining behavioral symptomatology, histological data, central nervous system function, and auditory linguistic skills. Because a lack of speech and language development is frequently the only presenting symptom, and because responses to auditory stimuli among children with such symptoms are sometimes inconsistent,[43] it is critical to determine whether a child can hear and whether he can attend to and appropriately integrate the sound stimuli in his environment.

The child with a peripheral hearing impairment is fairly readily identified. His consistent lack of response to sound is frequently recognized in infancy;[34] he usually startles consistently to sounds well above his threshold;[25] he uses gestures meaningfully, attends to facial expressions, responds to sound consistently, uses vocalizations projectively, and his vocalizations have a characteristic tonal quality.[40] If the child has a peripheral hearing impairment which is not further complicated by the presence of other kinds of disorders (either psychic or organic), he is usually "easy to test." Should the child not be "easy to test," however, his hearing impairment may be peripheral or non-peripheral in nature. According to a study by McHugh and McCoy, approximately fifty per cent of the children who failed to acquire speech by the age of two and one-half years were reported to have significant peripheral hearing impairment, and twenty-nine per cent were reported to be brain injured with hearing adequate to learn speech.[36] It is to a discussion of the audiological evaluation and education of the child with a non-peripheral hearing impairment that the remainder of this chapter will be devoted.

AUDIOLOGICAL EVALUATION
OF THE
NEUROLOGICALLY IMPAIRED CHILD

According to Ades, research on the central auditory pathway goes back only a few years into the last century.[1] This research has a much shorter history than the study of the other sensory systems, and the bulk of the more significant work has been accomplished only in the last three decades. This work has been heavily weighted in the study of pure tones, which are measured in the parameters of frequency and intensity. Most recently, however, there has been a growing trend away from pure tone studies of the central auditory system, with an increasing awareness that discrimination of tonal patterns (like speech) appears to be a cortically bound activity. Bocca states that there is ". . . a wide difference between the recognition of the physical qualities of a sound and the process of identification of a verbal pattern. The former depends upon the working of the auditory apparatus as a whole; the latter is a specific function of the auditory cortex."[7] That is, the different attributes of any sound must be transmitted with fidelity from the ear to the centers in order to be recognized accurately. In the case of a meaningful verbal message, however, ". . . it is also necessary that they [the sounds] reach the centers with a certain order in space and time."[7] Bocca continues, " 'Reversed' words are not comprehensible, in spite of the fact that they contain exactly the same frequencies and intensities; a poorly known foreign language is not understood if it is spoken rapidly."[7] Thus, for investigation of the functioning of the auditory cortex, ". . . pure tones and simple sounds must be abandoned, and words or sentences must be resorted to."[7]

An intact auditory cortex appears to be essential for maintaining attention to auditory signals. The question of attention was raised by Hubel *et al.*,[27] who reported that in the course of examining single unit responses from the cortices of cats (unrestrained and unanesthetized), they came upon a "population of cells that appears to be sensitive to auditory stimuli only if the cat 'pays attention' to the sound source." McHugh[35] states that the ability to pay attention demands a "certain organic and functional integrity of the central nervous system that appears to be lacking in many of these 'brain-injured' children." Thus, their lack of attention is presumed to be symptomatic of their disorder.

There have been studies which have reported peripheral hearing impairments among groups of children with overt evidence of positive neurological (motor and/or sensory) involvement.[28,50] Often, however, the child who is brought for an audiological evaluation has a communication impairment as his only presenting symptom. Ruling out mental retardation and/or emotional disturbance, a diagnosis of non-peripheral hearing impairment is often made when this impairment in communication is accompanied by a seeming disorder in the ability to attend to auditory stimuli rather than a disorder in the ability to hear them. In the past decade there has been a trend toward labeling these children as neurologically impaired, sometimes despite negative neurological findings.[38]

Attempts have been made to categorize these language disorders and to identify their related sites of lesion. As a result, a terminology has emerged in the literature which is lengthy and often contradictory. The following is a partial presentation of the terms currently in use, together with their different definitions. The reader will note the wide disparity among some of the definitions presented.

Aphasia

1. ". . . the inability to use and/or understand spoken language, . . . the result of damage or defect in the central nervous system."[37,38] The thresholds shown by standard audiometric techniques and by EDR audiometry are often widely disparate.[37] Not synonymous with *central auditory disorder* or *central language disorder*.[37] Implies an additional language disability other than auditory.[37,38] The problem with the aphasic child is not in hearing sound but in understanding it.[5] *Aphasic* is the term applied to children with disorders of language development, analogous to the term *deaf*, which is applied to children with lack of normal auditory sensitivity.[22] "Aphasia . . . is the failure to utilize auditory signals delivered to the central nervous system for the understanding of spoken language."[23,32] Aphasia is a type of inhibition to hearing in which "sound cannot be imitated for communication and so is rejected as useless."[9]

2. ". . . must be considered an auditory disorder." The various *aphasoid* conditions exist from birth and are undoubtedly the result of a defect in the central nervous system.[17]

3. ". . . an impairment or loss in the comprehension or use of language for symbolization or ideation, which is acquired after the develop-

ment of language."[16] The term should be restricted to describe an acquired deficit.[42]

4. Receptive aphasia is a deficiency in the interpretation of auditory impulses after they have been delivered to the higher brain centers. Some aphasic children learn to ignore sound because it has no meaning to them. Thus, they may be presumed to be deaf.[39,40,41]

Auditory Agnosia

1. Indicative of gross damage to the auditory cortex. . . . a relatively rare condition in which the child cannot attach meaning to any sound though he has normal auditory acuity (Myklebust.[25])

2. Synonymous with congenital word deafness. Exists in presence of normal hearing. Clinical features include lack of speech or limited speech, inability to comprehend words by the auditory route. Lesion is apparently in the audito-psychic area of Wernicke's area of the brain.[29]

Dysacusis

1. An impairment of hearing that is not primarily a loss of auditory sensitivity. *Dysacusic disorders* are: central auditory imperception and auditory agnosia, which differ, primarily, in severity. Dysacusis differs from aphasia, which is acquired after the development of language.[16,20,30]

2. Dysacusis is used to describe a defect in audition which is usually central and on an integrative or interpretive level. It could be reserved as a general heading for many varieties of central communication defects including: aphasia, word deafness, psychogenic deafness, mind deafness, etc.[24]

3. Central imperception, including the brain-injured child and the child with cerebral palsy. To be differentiated from *word deafness and aphasia*.[31]

Central Deafness

1. Exists in presence of an injury to the auditory cortex.[17]

2. Auditory pathways in the central nervous system have been impaired and nerve impulses do not reach interpretation area in auditory cortex (Myklebust.[25])

3. "Central deafness by definition, is a form of neurological impairment."[48]

Clinical experience would seem to corroborate the descriptions in the literature (despite the frequent contradictions) of a heterogeneous group of children, with lack of speech development, who show evidence of apparent non-peripheral hearing impairment. Behaviorally, these children may exhibit one or a combination of several of the following characteristics.

1. Hyperactivity or hypoactivity.
2. Inconsistency
3. Perseveration
4. Distractibility
5. Withdrawal
6. Delayed response
7. Motor impairment

There is close agreement that the term *differential diagnosis of auditory disorders* in these children is often used to indicate *differential diagnosis of language disorders*[21] (or differential diagnosis of "listening" disorders). These children evidence difficulty in attending to auditory stimuli and frequently cannot be tested to the satisfaction of the audiologist. Children with communication difficulties or language disorders provide very complex diagnostic problems mainly because, "Our present knowledge of how a sound stimulus is received, analyzed, transmitted, perceived, integrated and synthesized into speech, thought production, emotional response or appropriate motor activity is very incomplete."[34] Frisina states that *auditory-perceptual disturbance* is a term frequently heard but that ". . . to this date there has not been an objective analysis of the phenomenon."[21]

McHugh[35] reflected the opinion of a number of investigators when he stated that the irregular difficulties these children exhibit in the development of verbal or other forms of language "appear to be the effects or subtle expressions of minimal brain damage or dysfunction." If these children are brain injured or neurologically impaired, surely their ability to hear can be neither evaluated nor expressed in terms of a decibel loss. Rather, an interpretation of the total effect of auditory stimuli upon the child's perceptual, emotional, intellectual and motor behavior should be attempted.[34] Bocca and Calearo[8] have stated that, "The central auditory function consists precisely in the capacity to organize simultaneous or successive elements into a definite pattern." Therefore, they say that the investigation of dysfunction at the level of the central auditory system should deal with "the evaluation of disorders of pattern formation and integration, by means of appropriate test material, and not upon the capacity to discriminate between single sound elements." Bordley[9] cautions that the examiner observe whether the child has a readiness to listen, whether he has an apparent readiness to talk, and whether he has communicative awareness, never forgetting that a careful case history from the mother is sometimes worth many tests. Myklebust[41] warns that the assumption that a diagnosis can be made by assessing only the child's response to sound must be seriously questioned. Rather, the total behavioral pattern should be analyzed.

In addition to the important consideration of differentiating between peripheral and non-peripheral impairment of hearing, Davis[12] points out that, "two defects, [perhaps a mild peripheral deficit plus a non-peripheral deficit] neither of which would produce a significant impairment of itself, may add to produce a very considerable overall impairment and handicap." McHugh[35] reports that, in brain-injured children, abrupt high frequency losses or moderate flat losses of hearing sensitivity seem to have a more disturbing overall effect on ability to learn verbal language than the same degree of partial sensory deprivation in a child with an undamaged brain.

And so, faced with a *non-verbal* child[43] with questionable hearing, if this child is difficult to test, the audiologist must depend upon creative audiometry and a multi-disciplinary approach in order to arrive at a differential diagnosis. Despite advances and developments in audiology, our evaluative techniques are still quite primitive. Whether or not the child presents demonstrable evidence of neurological impairment (by way of obvious motor impairment or by a report of positive neurological findings), by use of a qualitative rather than a strictly quantitative approach, the audiologist must attempt to separate the peripheral from the non-peripheral aspects of hearing impairment. Using play audiometry techniques, this can be accomplished in a variety of ways. How does the child respond to silence? How does the child respond to sound after a period of silence? Does the child startle at high intensities? Does the child respond to quiet sounds and not to loud ones? Inasmuch as the non-verbal child cannot be tested by speech audiometry procedures, can he respond appropriately to tonal sequences and patterns? Does the child demonstrate the ability to use abstract behavior in an auditory field?

The answers to these and other such questions can provide the audiologist with the kind of qualitative information about the child which, when viewed together with information from the speech pathologist, neurologist, psychologist, and psychiatrist, can provide a meaningful diagnostic impression about the child. The test situation should be carefully organized for the child, and the child should be "structured or organized in the test situation."[34] Much patience is certainly required in testing these children, and it may take a number of different tests and test situations before conclusions can be reached. McHugh[35] strongly states that, with brain injured children, "an early, exact, diagnosis is difficult, and in many cases it may be impossible until the child has reached a stage of maturity or reorganization of this central nervous system which permits a reasonable assessment of his special communicative difficulties."

EDUCATIONAL CONSIDERATIONS

Vernon[48] indicated that the schools for the deaf in the United States reported an enrollment of 1,293 neurologically impaired children (including those with cerebral palsy and aphasia) in 1959, and indicated that this number is growing steadily. The conditions of neurological impairment are not always obvious, but the problem is quite serious because it frequently results in academic disabilities and behavior problems. In 1958 Goldstein[22] stated that educational programs for deaf children may not be adequate. They would probably benefit from programs geared toward language development and the general handling of auditory stimuli.

Serious question has been raised as to the educational usefulness of differentiating between and among some of the previously stated and defined auditory disorders. Brutten, while raising such question, stated,

The difficulty is compounded by a widespread uncertainty as to what

portions of the auditory mechanisms are involved in so-called peripheral deafnesses and where the lesions occur that give rise to a central
language disorder. In some quarters, aphasic or "aphasoid" conditions
are considered to be related to cortical damage. But more and more
youngsters are being classified as cases of central auditory imperception
although their problems may relate to a lesion which is assumed to be
quite peripheral . . . .[11]

   Though the facilities available for the education of the hear-
ing-impaired child with neurological damage are few indeed,
there is agreement among a number of authorities that differential
diagnosis of hearing and language disorders should be geared
toward educational therapy,[22,31] and differential diagnosis should
be an on-going process so that tentative formulations can be
revised after observing the child's response to training with specific teaching methods.[11,37,38]

REFERENCES

1. Ades, H. W.: Central auditory mechanisms. In *Handbook of Physiology.*
   Washington, 1959, Vol. 1, Sec. 1, pp. 585-613.
2. American Academy Ophthalmology and Otolaryngology. *A Guide to the
   Care of Adults with Hearing Loss.* Rochester, 1960.
3. Barr, B.: Pure tone audiometry for pre-school children, a preliminary
   report. *Acta Otolaryng (Stockholm),* Suppl. 110, 1954.
4. Barr, B.: Pure tone audiometry for pre-school children. *Acta Otolaryng
   (Stockholm),* Suppl. 121, 1955.
5. Barry, H.: *The Young Aphasic Child.* Washington, The Volta Bureau,
   1961.
6. Bloomer, H.: A simple method for testing the hearing of small children.
   J Speech Hearing Dis, 7:311, 1942.
7. Bocca, E.: Clinical aspects of cortical deafness. International Conference
   of Audiology, May 13-16, 1957, St. Louis. *Laryngoscope, 68* (3) :301-09,
   1958.
8. Bocca, E., and Calearo, C.: Central hearing processes. In Jerger, James
   (Ed.): *Modern Developments in Audiology.* New York, Academic,
   1963, pp. 337-70.
9. Bordley, J.: Evaluation of hearing in preschool children, a Symposium:
   Deafnes in Children — Knowledge and Practice, *Trans Amer Acad
   Ophthal Otolaryng, 61* (6) :706-07, 1957.
10. Bordley, J.; Hardy, W. G., and Richter, C. P.: Audiometry with the use
    of galvanic skin-resistance response. *Bull Hopkins Hosp, 82*:569, May
    1948.

11. Brutten, M.: Some problems relating to differential diagnosis of auditory disorders in children. *Report of Proceedings of the 39th Meeting of the Convention of the American Instructors of the Deaf.* Washington, U.S. Gov. Printing Office, 1960, pp. 37-43.

12. David, H.: A functional classification of auditory defects. *Trans Amer Otol Soc, 50:*98-111, 1962.

13. DiCarlo, L. M.; Kendall, D. C., and Goldstein, R.: Diagnostic procedures for auditory disorders in children. *Folia Phoniat (Basel), 14:*206-64, 1962.

14. Dix, M. R., and Hallpike, C. S.: The peep show. *Brit Med J,* Nov. 8, 1947, pp. 719-23.

15. Doctor, P. V.: Multiple handicaps. *Report of Proceedings of the 39th Meeting of the Convention of the American Instructors of the Deaf.* Washington, U.S. Gov. Printing Office, 1960, pp. 34-37.

16. Douglas, F. M.; Fowler, E. P., Jr., and Ryan, G. M.: *A Differential Study of Communication Disorders in a School for the Deaf,* A research project conducted at St. Joseph's School for the Deaf and the Speech and Hearing Clinic. New York, Columbia-Presbyterian Medical Center, 1961.

17. Conservation of Hearing Committee, Pennsylvania Academy of Ophthalmology and Otolaryngology. Etiologic factors in auditory disorders in children. *Penn Med J, 63:*203-04, 1960.

18. Ewing, I. R.: Deafness in infancy and early childhood. *J Laryn, 58:* 4-137, 1943.

19. Ewing, I. R., and Ewing, A. W. G.: The ascertainment of deafness in infancy and early childhood. *J Laryn, 59:*309, 1944.

20. Fowler, E. P., Jr., and Kastein, S.: Hypoacusis, dysacusis and retardation. *Res Publ Ass Res Nerv Ment Dis, 39:*270-85, 1962.

21. Frisina, R. D.: Measurement of hearing in children. In Jerger, James (Ed.): *Modern Developments in Audiology.* New York, Academy, 1963, pp. 126-166.

22. Goldstein, R.: Differential classification of disorders of communication in children. *Amer Ann Deaf, 103* (2) :215-223, 1958.

23. Goldstein, R.: The role of electrophysiologic audiometry in the differential diagnosis of deafness and aphasia in children. *Acta Audiologica Y Foniatrica Hispenoamericana. 4* (1) :3-13, 1962.

24. Goodhill, V.: Pathology, diagnosis and therapy of deafness. In Travis, L. (Ed.) : *Handbook of Speech Pathology.* New York, Appleton, 1957, pp. 313-88.

25. International Conference on Audiology, a panel discussion. Hearing in children. May 13-16, 1957, St. Louis. *Laryngoscope, 68* (3) :218-53, 1958.

26. Hirsh, I.: *The Measurement of Hearing.* New York, McGraw, 1952.

27. Hubel, D. H.; Henson, A. R., and Galambos, R.: "Attention" units in

the auditory cortex. *Science, 129* (3358) :1279-80, 1959.

28. Hyman, C. B., and Keaster, J.: Hearing loss in children with neonatal hyperbilirubinemia. *J Amer Med Wom Ass, 17* (9) :733-4, 1962.

29. Karlin, I. W.: Congenital verbal—auditory agnosia (word deafness). *Pediatrics, 7* (1) :60-8, 1951.

30. Kastein, S., and Fowler, E. P., Jr.: Differential diagnosis in children with communication disorders. A film demonstration. *Trans Amer Acad Ophthal Otolaryng*, pp. 529-39, 1960.

31. Kastein, S., and Fowler, E. P., Jr.: Differential diagnosis of communication disorders in children referred for hearing tests. *AMA Arch Otolaryng, 60* (4) :468-77, 1954.

32. Landau, W. M.; Goldstein, R., and Kleffner, F. R.: Congenital aphasia, a clinicopathologic study. *Neurology (Minneap), 10* (10) :915-21, 1960.

33. Mark, H. J.: Two symptoms pathognomonic for congenital central communication disorders in children. *J Pediat, 55* (3) :391-6, 1959.

34. McHugh, H. E.: Problems of testing and managing children with communication difficulties, a symposium: deafness in children — Knowledge and Practice. *Trans Amer Acad Ophthal Otolaryng, 61* (6) : 708-10, 1957.

35. McHugh, H. E.: The brain-injured child with impaired hearing. *Laryngoscope, 71* (9) :1034-57, 1961.

36. McHugh, H. E., and McCoy, R. H.: The evaluation of hearing in preschool children who lack normal speech. *Laryngoscope, 64* :845-60, October, 1954.

37. Monsees, E.: Aphasia and deafness in children. *Exceptional Child, 25* (9) : 395-9, 409-10, 1959.

38. Monsees, E.: Aphasia in children, diagnosis and education. *Volta Review, 59* (9) :392-414, 1957.

39. Myklebust, H. R.: Aphasia in children — diagnosis and training. In Travis, L. (Ed.) : *Handbook of Speech Pathology.* New York, Appleton, 1957, pp. 514-30.

40. Myklebust, H. R.: *Auditory Disorders in Children.* New York, Grune, 1954.

41. Myklebust, H. R.: Differential diagnosis of deafness in young children. *J Exceptional Child, 17* (4) :97-117, 1951.

42. Rapin, I.: Neurological aspects, in *The Concept of Congenital Aphasia from the Standpoint of Dynamic Differential Diagnosis,* a symposium. Washington, American Speech and Hearing Association. 1959, pp. 21-5.

43. Reichstein, J.: Auditory threshold consistency in differential diagnosis of aphasia in children. *J Speech Hearing Dis, 29* (2) :147-55, 1964.

44. Suzuki, T.; Kamijo, Y., and Kiuchi, S.: Auditory test of newborn infants. *Ann Otol*, pp. 914-23, 1964.

45. Suzuki, T., and Ogiba, Y.: A technique of pure tone audiometry for

children under three years of age — Conditioned orientation reflex (COR). *Rev Laryng (Bordeaux), 81* (1-2) :33-45, 1960.

46. Thorne, B.: Conditioning children for pure tone testing. *J Speech Hearing Dis, 27* (1) :84-5, 1962.

47. Utley, J.: Suggestive procedures for determining auditory acuity in very young acoustically handicapped children. *Eye Ear Nose and Throat Monthly, 28* (12) :590-5, 1949.

48. Vernon, M.: The brain-injured (neurologically impaired) deaf child: a discussion of the significance of the problem, its symptoms and causes in deaf children. *Amer Ann Deaf, 106* (2) :239-50, 1961.

49. Withrow, F. B., and Goldstein, R.: An electrophysiologic procedure for determination of threshold in children. *Laryngoscope, 68:*1674-99, 1958.

50. Zaner, A., and Miller, M.: Hearing problems in athetoid cerebral palsy. *AMA Arch Otolaryng, 70:*776-8, 1959.

SUPPLEMENTARY READING LIST

1. Adler, S.: *The Non-Verbal Child.* Springfield, Thomas, 1964.

2. Arnold, G.: Angeborene worttaubheit: akustische agnosie (congenital acoustic agnosis) . *Z Laryng Rhinol Otol, 39* (1) :53-9, 1960.

3. Bangs, E.: Evaluating children with language delay. *J Speech Hearing Dis, 26* (1) :6-18, 1961.

4. Barger, W. C.: Complications encountered in diagnosing the deaf child. In Ewing, Sir Alexander (Ed.) : *The Modern Educational Treatment of Deafness.* Manchester University Press, 1960.

5. Blakeley, R. W.: Erythroblastosis and perceptive hearing loss; responses of athetoids to tests of cochlear function. *J Speech Hearing Res, 2* (1) : 5-15, 1959.

6. Cody, D. T. R., and Bickford, R. G.: Cortical audiometry: an objective method of evaluating auditory acuity in man. *Proc Mayo Clin, 40* (4) : 273-87, 1965.

7. Connor, L. E.: Diagnostic teaching — the teacher's new role. *Volta Review, 61:*311-15, 1959.

8. Davis, H., and Silverman, S. R.: *Hearing and Deafness.* New York, Holt, 1960.

9. DiCarlo, L. M.: Hearing and Speech aspects. In *The Concept of Congenital Aphasia from the Standpoint of Dynamic Differential Diagnosis, a Symposium.* Washington, American Speech and Hearing Association, 1959, pp. 26-32.

10. DiCarlo, L. M.: Differential diagnosis of congenital aphasia. *Volta Review, 62:*361-4, 1960.

11. DiCarlo, L. M., and Bradley, W. H.: A simplified auditory test for infants and young children. *Laryngoscope,* 1961, 71/6 (628-646) .

12. Downs, M., and Doster, M. E.: A hearing test program for preschool children. *Rocky Mountain Med J, 56* (9) :37-9, 1959.
13. Duffy, J. K.: Hearing Problems of infancy and early childhood. *J Rehab Asia, 4* (2) :43-5, 1963.
14. Eagles, R. L., and Doerfler, L. G.: Hearing in children: acoustic performance. *J Speech Hearing Res, 4* (2) :149-63, 1961.
15. Eisenberg, R.: Electroencephalography in the study of developmental disorders of communication. *J Speech Hearing Dis, 31* (2) :183-6, 1966.
16. Eisenberg, R.; Griffin, E.; Coursin, D., and Hunter, M. A.: Auditory behavior in the human neonate: a preliminary report. *J Speech Hearing Res, 7* (3) :245-69, 1964.
17. Ewing, A. W. B.: Central deafness pedagogy. *International Audiology, 1:* 106-11, 1962.
18. Filling, S.: Differential diagnosis of hearing and language disturbance in children. *International Audiology, 1:*88-94, 1962.
19. Fowler, E. P., Jr.: Hearing impairment in a medical center population. *Arch Otolaryng (Chicago), 73:*295-300, March 1961.
20. Frisina, D. R.: Audiometric evaluation and its relation to habilitation and rehabilitation of the deaf. *Amer Ann Deaf,* 478-481.
21. Goldstein, R.: Special audiometric tests: their educational significance. *Amer Ann Deaf,* pp. 478-81, 1962.
22. Goldstein, R.; Kendall, D. C., and Arick, B. E.: Electroencephalic audiometry in young children. *J Speech Hearing Dis, 28* (4) :331-54, 1963.
23. Goldstein, R.; Landau, W. M., and Kleffner, F. R.: Neurologic assessment of some deaf and aphasic children. *Trans Amer Otol Soc, 46:* 122-36, 1958.
24. Goldstein, R.; Landau, W. M., and Kleffner, F. R.: Neurologic observations on a population of deaf and aphasic children. *Ann Otol, 69* (3) : 756-67, 1960.
25. Goodman, W. S.; Appleby, S. V.; Scott, J. W., and Ireland, P. E.: Audiometry in newborn children by electroencephalography. *Laryngoscope, 74* (9) :1319-28, 1964.
26. Grings, W. M.; Lowell, E. L., and Honnard, R. R.: Electrodermal responses of deaf children. *J Speech Hearing Res, 3* (2) :120-9, 1960.
27. Hardy, W. G.; Hardy, J. B.; Brinker, C. H.; Frazier, T. M., and Dougherty, A.: Auditory screenings of infants. *Trans Amer Otol Soc, 50:* 172-81, 1962.
28. Harris, R.: Central auditory functions in children. *Percept Motor Skills, 16* (1) :204-14, 1963.
29. Jerger, J.: Audiological manifestations of lesions in the auditory nervous system. *Laryngoscope, 70* (4) :417-25, 1960.
30. Kanadani, M.: Studies on PGSR audiometry. II Results of examinations in young children with severe hearing loss by PGSR audiometry, play

auditometry and startle reflex test. *J Otorhinolaryng Soc Jap, 62* (9) : 1951-57, 1959.

31. Kirk, S. A., and McCarthy, J. J.: The Illinois test of psycholinguistic abilities — an approach to differential diagnosis. *Amer J Ment Defic, 66* (3) :399-412, 1961.

32. McHugh, H. E.: Hearing and language disorders in children. *Postgrad Med, 31*:54-65, 1962.

33. Merklein, R. A., and Briskey, R. J.: Audiometric findings in children referred to a program for language disorders. *Volta Review, 64*:294-8, 1962.

34. Miller, M. H., and Polisar, I. A.: *Audiological Evaluation of the Pediatric Patient.* Springfield, Thomas, 1964.

35. Monsees, E. K.: Aphasia in children. *J Speech Hearing Dis, 26* (1) :83-6, 1961.

36. Monsees, E. K.: Aphasia and deafness in children — some aspects of differential diagnosis. *Clin Proc Child Hosp* (Wash) , *15* (11) :269-76, 1959.

37. Moss, J. W. *et al.*: Electrodermal response audiometry with mentally defective children. *J Speech Hearing Res, 4* (1) :41-7, 1961.

38. Myklebust, H. R., and Boshes, B.: Psychoneurological learning disorders in children. *Arch Pediat,* pp. 247-56, June, 1960.

39. Olson, J. L.: A comparison of sensory aphasic, expressive aphasic, and deaf children on the Illinois test of language ability. Unpublished doctoral dissertation, University of Illinois, 1960.

40. O'Neill, J. J.; Oyer, H. J., and Hillis, J. W.: Audiometric procedures used with children. *J Speech Hearing Dis, 26* (1) :61-6, 1961.

41. Pasnikowski, T.: The testing of the sense of hearing by means of electroencephalography. *Otolaryng Pol, 19* (1) :55-61, 1965.

42. Penfield, W., and Roberts, L.: *Speech and Brain-Mechanisms.* Princeton, Princeton, 1959.

43. Price, L. L., and Goldstein, R.: Averaged evoked responses for measuring auditory sensitivity in children. *J. Speech Hearing Dis, 31* (3) :248-56, 1966.

44. Rapin, Isabelle: Evoked responses to clicks in a group of children with communication disorders. *Ann NY Acad Sci, 112*:182-203, 1964.

45. Reichstein, J., and Rosenstein, J.: Differential diagnosis of auditory deficits — a review of the literature. *Exceptional Child, 31* (2) :73-82, 1964.

46. Sortini, A. J.: Hearing evaluation of brain-damaged children. *Volta Review, 62*:536-40, 1960.

47. Shere, M. O.: The cerebral-palsied child with a hearing loss. *Volta Review, 62* (8) :438-41, 1960.

48. Strauss, A. A., and Lehtinen, L. E.: *Psychopathology and Education of The Brain-Injured child.* New York, Grune, 1947.

49. Suzuki, T., and Taguchi, K.: Cerebral-evoked response to auditory stimuli in waking man. *Ann Otol, 74*:128-39, 1965.
50. Taylor, I. G.: *Neurological Mechanisms of Hearing and Speech in Children*. Washington, The Volta Bureau, 1964.
51. Whitehurst, M. W.: Testing the hearing of preschool children. *Volta Review, 63*:430-2, 463, 1961.
52. Williams, W. G., and Graham, J. T.: EEG responses to auditory stimuli in waking children. *J Speech Hearing Res, 6* (1) :57-63, 1963.

III

PSYCHOLOGICAL DEFICIT

Morton Bortner

THERE ARE TWO MAJOR ISSUES with which the psychological evaluation of brain-injured children can be concerned: (1) What does psychological information contribute to the making of a diagnosis of brain injury? (2) Given the fact of brain injury, what are the psychological strengths and weaknesses of the child? This chapter will be restricted to a discussion of the second question.

BRAIN INJURY DEFINED MEDICALLY

Since this chapter will consider the role of psychology after the establishment of a diagnosis of brain injury has been made, it is desirable to indicate briefly by what means such a diagnosis is established on a medical basis. There are, in general, four sources of information by means of which such a diagnosis may be reached. None of these sources is unequivocal, nor does any special combination of them result necessarily in an utterly secure statement. Most conclusions regarding brain and behavior are based on inference, unless direct observation is possible — such as in cases of surgical intervention, or in structural changes observed by roentgenogram, or at autopsy. The following represent sources of inference from which a judgment must be made. Obviously, such judgments will be influenced by the biases and the nature of the professional development of the judge.

Historical Information

If it can be established that the child was exposed at some point in his history to conditions of risk, then we may sometimes deduce that his present defective or deviant behavior is attributable to the known condition. Conditions of risk include those before, during, or after birth. Common examples of risk during pregnancy include rubella and toxemia; during birth, instrument delivery is sometimes implicated in the later development of central nervous system dysfunction; and after birth such conditions as encephalitis and trauma are often associated with later behavioral changes and central nervous system dysfunction. These examples are merely illustrative. Detailed information needs to be obtained by the physician about the conditions of pregnancy, birth, and the neonatal period; the occurrences of infections, illnesses, and injuries need to be documented.

It should be noted that these conditions of risk do not uniformly lead to altered or deviant behavior. Many children exposed to such risk develop normally. Further, it is well-known that when we need to rely on parental report to establish the occurrence of a given condition (or previous symptoms from which we may *infer* the existence of a condition) we are limited by errors in recollection. Despite these limitations, documentation of historical antecedents remains as a powerful tool in differential diagnosis.

Developmental Abnormalities

A second source of information from which a diagnosis may be inferred consists of the description of subtle deviations from expected development. These are sometimes called "soft signs." Common examples include mild tremor, poor physical coordination or awkwardness, exaggerated deep tendon reflexes and nystagmus. These listed symptoms are merely illustrative, and the developmental neurologist routinely includes in his examination a search for evidence such as the above examples that suggest diffuse as well as focal lesions.

Neurological Signs

The neurological examination can establish the integrity of the spinal cord, cerebellum, cranial nerves, basal ganglia, pyramidal system, and a variety of sensory systems. The relationship between function in these systems and behavior is not known. The neurologist faced with a child who has positive neurological signs and behavioral dysfunction will often make an inference about the origin of this behavioral dysfunction. That is, if brain injury is diagnosed as a result of positive findings in any of the above-named systems, and if aberrant behavior is also observed, then it is often inferred that the behavior is caused by brain injury. As Kennedy and Ramirez[17] have stated, this may be "guilt by association." The neurological examination, while it can establish the presence of neurological dysfunction as manifested by signs in the various systems of the central nervous system, cannot directly establish the basis for behavioral aberration.

Electroencephalography and Pneumoencephalography

Electroencephalography is helpful in establishing the existence of focal lesions. It is less successful with more diffuse lesions. It is based on the assumption that there is a correlation between the structure of the brain and its function as expressed on an electrical level. This relationship has proved to be disappointing, and it is reported that between fifteen and forty per cent of normal children show "abnormal"[17] records.

Pneumoencaphalography is helpful when structural changes in the skull are observable, but the number of cases where this is possible is very small.

PERTINENT PSYCHOLOGICAL FUNCTIONS

What are the pertinent psychological functions that deserve close scrutiny, and how are they to be evaluated? The requirement of pertinence limits discussion, in this context, to those functions that are relevant to education.

General Intelligence

An estimation of the child's general level of intellectual functioning is valuable because of the estimate of upper learning limits implied by the IQ and because of the estimate of the present level of learning capacity suggested by the mental age. Such estimates are no more irrevocable for these children than they are for normal children, nor are they any less functional. Despite their functional utility, criticisms are often voiced at their use with brain-injured children. A criticism commonly leveled is that they represent an unfair estimate in a child with a handicap. The particular handicaps most often referred to are motor and perceptual. Indeed, both motor and perceptual handicaps will have a lowering effect on those test scores which reflect either motor skills or perceptual intactness. However, it is noteworthy that no one seriously questions the ability of the examiner to circumvent the interference of certain motor handicaps in the assessment of intelligence in intellectually normal children. For example, a child without the use of hand function can be assessed for intelligence if the examiner relies on verbal tasks. Certainly, a similar approach should be no less effective for many brain-injured children whose performance scores (especially timed scores) are rendered questionable because of the interference of motor incoordination.

It is another matter when a child has a perceptual handicap. Whereas we can justifiably omit performance tasks in favor of a verbal estimate for children with impaired motor function, it is harder to justify the omission of perceptual tasks. As perceptual functioning is so inextricably bound up with intelligence itself, its assessment cannot be avoided or deferred.

An estimate of the general level of intelligence serves as a context within which specific deficits are better understood. For example, severe deficit in concept usage in a child with severe mental deficiency is an entirely different matter than in a child with mild retardation. Further, the general intelligence test provides the vehicle by means of which it is possible to compare verbal with non-verbal abilities. Although individual differences are great, there is a tendency in this population for verbal scores to exceed non-verbal scores. This is in contrast to the normal tendency to score approximately the same in both verbal and non-verbal areas. Moreover, the intelligence profiles of *these* retarded children are the reverse of what is considered characteristic of retarded children without neurological impairment. In the latter children, non-verbal scores exceed verbal scores. The rule of thumb commonly accepted in many clinical settings as an indication of brain injury is a discrepancy of twenty or more IQ points in favor of verbal ability. Special difficulties with block-design type tasks, such as are found in the Wechsler Intelligence Scale for Children, are considered pathognomonic, and there is a subliterature concerned with this narrow but apparently important problem area.

Much research has been concerned with the search for a more detailed and enlightening pathognomonic pattern — something beyond the verbal-non-verbal discrepancy. Such efforts seem especially fruitless in the light of the emerging recognition that "brain injury" subsumes a variety of clinical conditions. Clearly, no one pattern can be expected to characterize diverse conditions. However, the examination of an individual's pattern of abilities may be quite fruitful. Omnibus type tests, particularly the Wechsler Intelligence Scale for Children and the Stanford-Binet (with somewhat more effort on the part of the examiner) lend themselves to the construction of profiles. These profiles are a step beyond the verbal-non-verbal dichotomy and provide us with the opportunity to compare a variety of cognitive functions such as vocabulary, comprehension, concept usage, social judgment, attention and concentration, and various aspects of perception. Crude as such comparisons must be, they can be helpful to teachers looking for points of departure around which to plan special instruction. When these descriptions are not concrete, the teacher is left with a series of generalizations which are less helpful than they might be. For example, rather than describe a child as having a deficit in *memory* it is possible (especially with the Stanford-Binet) to distinguish between memory for words, objects, pictures, digits, or ideas. Such specificity, while not necessary for normal children, seems to be both necessary and helpful in the description of brain-injured children, for the simple reason that they show task-specific performance. So, it is not uncommon to find, within the perceptual area, difficulty with one perceptual test and no difficulty with another perceptual test. Only a task-specific description of performance will remove the implication of contradictory findings.

Fluctuations in performance are often ascribed to these children. So, for example, good performance on a given task on a particular day may be followed by poor performance at a later time. Clinical experience rather than empirical research is the basis for this description, and a number of basic questions remain unanswered at this time. For example, in what psychological processes, in what achievement areas, and to what extent, do fluctuations exist? Despite the lack of systematic information on the nature of the problem, a problem apparently exists. Teachers frequently report their frustration in dealing with the child who can perform a task on one day but not on the next. Until we know more about the kinds and amounts of fluctuations which exist in these children, the time intervals which define them, and the processes underlying inadequate performance, it will not be feasible to use the concept of fluctuation in a manner helpful to teachers.

Unfortunately, downward fluctuation is sometimes misperceived by the teacher as representing a loss of interest, or more generally, as a change in motivational status. After all, if the child can perform on one occasion, why not on a later occasion? The less-experienced teacher may also anticipate incorrectly that success on task *A* will be accompanied by success on task *B* when both tasks are at the same difficulty level. The fact that this is not always the case is probably another example of the task-specificity of performance referred to earlier. Such specificity of performance makes the child appear inconsistent or unpredictable for psychodynamic reasons. There are occasions when children display such inconsistencies for psychodynamic reasons rather than cognitive reasons, and it therefore becomes a task for evaluation to distinguish between these two bases for behavior.

Attention and Concentration

It is generally recognized that performance in almost any cognitive activity involves some element of attention and concentration. In addition to its ubiquitous quality, this element is considered an entity and therefore is measurable. The digit-span and the arithmetic subtests of the Wechsler Intelligence Scale for Children are considered indicators of attention and concentration. Attention is also considered an explanatory concept. So, in research on double simultaneous stimulation, the fact that many brain-injured patients respond to only one stimulus even though two stimuli have been presented is explained by some as being the result of inadequate or selective attention.[11]

The value of the concept of attention may be more descriptive than explanatory since, in its present usage, it does not explain *why* a subject attends to a particular stimulus and not to another. It is clear that the concept of attention is not yet clear. Therefore, it may be less valuable to describe a child as generally inattentive than to advance some hypotheses as to why he is inattentive. If that is not possible, perhaps facts can be stated regarding what he is or isn't attentive to. Additionally, it may be fruitful to evaluate those environmental or contextual conditions facilitating or adverse, which seem to exert influence on attention. This kind of information may have implications for the teacher in her choice of materials. For example, young children generally are able to attend to three-dimensional objects for longer periods of time than to drawings or pictures. The use of colorful materials also seems to be accepted as helpful in gaining and holding attention.

Instructional procedures may be structured to deal with a particular attentional deficit. For example, the simultaneous presentation of two or more stimuli is frequently used as a means of teaching the concept of class or category. For children with attentional defects which prevent comprehension under conditions of simultaneous stimulation, a sequential presentation would constitute an alternate route. These examples are offered only for illustrative purposes. The point is that the more clearly defined the deficit, the more likely it is that instructional countermeasures will be found.

Distractibility

Distractibility is a frequent clinical finding in these children, but this may be a label without too much educational utility if it is seen as an arbitrary shift in attention. If, instead, it is seen as a motivated shift of attention from one focus to another, the psychologist can set himself the task of discovering what type of stimuli the child prefers or can attend to, and what type of stimuli fails to hold his attention. Further, it may be asked what the contextual conditions are which facilitate attention on a particular stimulus, as contrasted with those conditions which seem to favor or at least permit distractibility.

Another way to view the inattention-distractibility problem is as a failure of inhibition. The normal child is vaguely aware at all times of a multiplicity of incoming stimuli — the chair he is sitting on, noises in the hall, hunger or thirst, street sounds, and the touch of his clothing on his body yet he is able to suppress or inhibit overt responses to these stimuli in the interest of attending to something the teacher is saying. The failure to inhibit is manifested as a flow of responsiveness to various stimuli irrelevant to classroom instruction. Seen in this light, distractibility suggests the need to find tasks, materials, and situations which selectively facilitate response inhibition.

While some children shift too easily from one focus to another, others exhibit difficulty in shifting. For a brief time after an initial stimulus has been replaced with a second stimulus, these children continue to respond as if the initial stimulus were still there — that is, they perseverate. Perseveration may manifest itself both verbally and non-verbally. In testing, verbal perseverations are easily mistaken for lack of knowledge of a required answer. For example, in a vocabulary test, a perseverative child may, after defining a word, continue to give the same definition to later words even though the child knows better (as may be determined after the perseveration ceases). On a non-verbal level, test evidence of perseveration is seen in two ways: (1) A given design may be copied repetitiously even though only one response is required, and (2) The child may respond to a series of designs to be copied in sequence by fixing on one design and inappropriately repeating the same response, despite the removal of the triggering stimulus and its replacement with later designs in the sequence.

Still other children attend to unimportant aspects of a stimulus, and neglect the major features. This is sometimes referred to as figure-ground disturbance. An illustration of this behavior may be seen in the response of the child who, called upon to identify a picture stimulus of a girl, answered *button*. Indeed, the girl's blouse did contain a button. This type of response may be seen as a problem in atypical focus of attention. This suggests that the teacher's task would be to help the child learn to shift the focus of his attention.

Activity Level

MEANING OF HYPERKINESIS

Although hyperkinesis is frequently reported as a major accompaniment of brain injury, there remains some ambiguity about this condition and the term itself. Does the term imply overactivity all the time, part of the time, or according to some pattern? Published studies do not provide sufficient objective evidence to answer these questions. In the main, they are based on parent and teacher reports and clinically observed behavior. Birch[3] hypothesized that brain-injured children may not be as overactive as they are poorly focused. He cites an unpublished paper by Schulman who quantified physical activity in a group of brain-injured children and in a normal comparison group; he found no significant differences between the groups. Might it be that brain-injured children are not more active than their normal peers, but simply are more likely to be noticed because of the nature of their activity? Clearly, there is a need for quantitative studies to clarify the amount, nature, and patterns of physical activity which characterize different groups of brain-injured children.

Another source of ambiguity about this condition derives from the readily observed variability of kinesis within a given child. A visit to any class of young brain-injured children will reveal some children moving about frantically without clear goals. If observed long enough, they will eventually be seen to settle down and work, or sit, or observe, or listen placidly for long periods of time. Whether these different modes of response can be attributed to changes in the environment or whether they are spontaneous and associated directly with neural dysfunction remains to be determined. Psychological evaluation of hyperkinesis in the classroom may well address itself to the question of devising and testing conditions designed to elicit placid and restrained behavior.

CONTINUUM OF DEFECT

The frequency with which hyperactivity occurs in clinical descriptions has probably derived in part from what Eisenberg[12] has called its "nuisance value." Clearly, hyperactivity in the class-room can be disruptive and will command the attention of the teacher and the clinician. It may be useful however, to conceive of this problem as existing on a continuum of defect in inhibition and excitation.[4] At the other end of the continuum is the hypo-activity so frequently associated with mongolism. Even here there is diversity of findings, and not all mongoloids are hypoactive and placid as they are usually reported to be.[6,30]

Perception

CONCERN WITH DIAGNOSIS

Clinicians have attributed special significance to perceptual adequacy and have linked it to basic neurophysiological intactness so that inadequate perception is seen as reflecting a damaged central nervous system. This linkage serves the function of provid-ing the examiner with a behavioral tool for establishing diagnosis of brain impairment. Unfortunately, all manner of complex re-sponses to diverse visual stimuli have been lumped together as "perceptual" behavior. While this type of generalization may be of value to the diagnostician in his search for a common process underlying diverse behavioral manifestations, it is clearly mislead-ing to the teacher who has to be concerned with the nature and the diversity of the manifestations themselves.

An examination of some current practices may illuminate this issue. Clinical perceptual tests usually require the child to dis-criminate, manipulate, or copy two or three-dimensional stimuli. Examples of such tests include Kohs Blocks (three-dimensional manipulation), Bender-Gestalt designs (two-dimensional copying), Discrimination of Forms, Stanford-Binet, Year IV (two-dimen-sional discrimination or recognition). Inadequate performance on any one or more of these diverse tests, despite the differences in task demands, has been traditionally interpreted as a basic perceptual inadequacy. This finding, in turn, has been one of the bases for the inferential diagnosis of brain injury. Such general information that a child has perceptual deficit is of little use to the teacher in her formulation of instructional procedures. A detailed consideration of the nature of the deficit is required. Clearly, the child who can't copy designs but who can match them is perceptually different (and more fortunate) than the child who can't even match accurately. The training of these two hypothetical children will follow quite different paths.

It seems desirable to develop categories of perceptual function which will communicate information to the teacher in terms that are educationally meaningful. There is a need for categories that are translatable into classroom learning experiences. Labels for such categories are implicit in the various perceptual tasks themselves. For example, the Stanford-Binet test of intelligence not only contains a variety of such perceptual tasks but also, by their arrangement according to age specificity, suggests a hierarchy of levels of perceptual development — from recognition of objects, through recognition of pictures of objects, through recognition of drawings of objects, through recognition of drawings of abstract designs. Such a hierarchy may, indeed, be a behavioral reflection of the development of the central nervous system itself. This concept of levels of central nervous system function stems from the writings of Hughlings Jackson.[16] Support for its applicability to perceptual processes is found in the research of Bortner and Birch[7] who found in brain-injured children that the ability to discriminate designs may be intact even though the ability to draw these same designs is impaired. They postulated two functionally autonomous systems — a recognition or discrimination system which develops earlier, and a perceptual-motor or more complex integrative system which develops later. Whether or not these findings represent basic processes, they at least appear to be translatable into classroom experiences.

In the absence of defined basic perceptual processes, the psychological evaluation can address itself to the refined description of a variety of perceptual responses such as the ability to match, draw designs, or manipulate objects in space. Deficits in any of these areas, when described in sufficient detail, lend themselves more readily and become more accessible to special instruction.

Concept Usage

Research on the concept usage of brain-injured children remains dominated by the theme developed largely by Vigotsky[29] and Goldstein[14] in their work with adults. The essence of this theme is that concrete thought, which is concerned with the immediate stimulus, is characteristic of brain-injured individuals; whereas, abstract thought, which goes beyond the given and which utilizes symbols, is a higher form of thinking rendered defective by injury to the brain. Reviews of research by Birch[3] and Gallagher[13] do not confirm this simple dichotomy as necessarily characteristic but, instead, report great variability among these children on a continuum of cognitive disability. Of equal interest is that when schizophrenic,[21] deaf,[19,23] and mentally retarded children[22] are studied, they also show difficulties in abstract thinking. Brain-injured children can make no exclusive claims to this disability. Hence, the diagnostic value of concrete thinking as a sign of brain injury seems to have lost some of its significance.

Since the behavior of aberrant individuals is so frequently interpreted as a regression to earlier levels of function characteristic of young children, it would be helpful to know the course of development of conceptual thinking in young children. Unfortunately, beyond the generalization that more difficult concepts are associated with increasing age, there is still disagreement on the age and stage specificity of abstract thinking.[25]

Moreover, it is clear from the work of Piaget and his followers that the developmental course of concept development depends, to some extent, on the nature of the concept being studied. They have studied the development of logic and reasoning, ideas of time, quantity, motion, speed, and physical causality. Development in each of these areas, while certainly related, follows an individual course. These areas of conceptual thinking are directly related to, and in some cases synonymous with, many classroom goals. It therefore seems plausible to suggest that the psychological evaluation of conceptual thinking in brain-injured children may profitably concern itself with the identification of the level or quality of conceptual thinking in each of these areas. Such evaluations would eliminate the need for building a bridge between clinical descriptions such as "concrete thinking" and the special instructional procedures which derive from such descriptions. Such evaluations would, in effect, deal with content which is directly related to instructional goals.

A note of caution to the examiner regarding the interpretation of concrete responses is implied by recent evidence[5] which indicates that response failure need not reflect incapacity. This study used a sorting technique to measure concept usage; it reported that the level of the child's concept usage was, in part, a reflection of the context of the question. Thus, children who, in one context, responded to sorting tasks in low level terms of form or color would, under altered conditions of testing, demonstrate a capacity for more abstract sorting behavior. The encouraging nature of these findings is in the implication that the selective restructuring of the task might result in higher order performance. If, for example, as was found in this study, the presence of color interferes with the child's capacity to formulate more abstract categories, then the instructional procedure can be structured in a way that takes cognizance of this fact.

Personality Status

Neurological damage or dysfunction does not, of course, preclude the existence of personality disorder. Disorders may include (1) psychotic or neurotic adjustments such as are found in children without neurological impairment and which are merely coincident with the child's neurological status, (2) reactions to the limitations imposed by the neurological impairment, and (3) reactions which stem directly from the impairment itself.

A certain amount of effort is usually expended on determining which of these three categories best describes a given child's condition; the most difficult problem is one of deciding whether or not a particular manifestation is coincident with or a direct result of brain damage. The teacher is perhaps somewhat less interested in this categorization and has more concern with the specifics of the child's psychodynamics.

What are these specifics for brain-damaged children in general? According to a recent summary[10] of the literature, their psychodynamic difficulties are manifested in a variety of negative emotional characteristics, relationship capacities, social behaviors, and variations in mood and adjustment. The wide range of this list of difficulties suggests that a great deal more than brain function is implicated. That is, the fact that poor interpersonal relations and social maladjustments are described suggests that the family and complex social phenomena are inextricably implicated in the production of their personality disturbances. The mere fact of handicap in a family is, in itself, hardly likely to have a salutary effect on intrafamilial attitudes. Moreover, whatever difficulties are. implicit in these children's primary disabilities are in interaction with family constellations.

We might add to the list of ingredients underlying the development of personality, the recent evidence[27] which emphasizes the variety of individual differences occurring on a constitutional basis and which gives rise to a number of discrete patterns of responsiveness. Some of these patterns — as manifested in children who are irregular in basic body functions, non-adaptive to changes in stimuli, intense in sensory reactions, withdrawn in initial responses to new people and situations, negative in mood, and active to a high degree — tend to produce problems in intrafamilial adjustments even in normal children. There is no reason to doubt that such patterns of individual responsiveness are not also present in children with brain damage, and that these patterns are initially in interaction with certain of their primary inadequacies and later interact with certain of their feelings about themselves. The context for this evolution of personal development is, of course, a family situation where parents demonstrate all shades of involvement, understanding and capacity for administering a household with a problem. The variance implied by such a possible range of forces is, of course, great and must be taken into consideration while one is searching for *the* personality dynamics of brain-injured children.

It follows from the foregoing that a comprehensive assessment of the personal dynamics of a brain-injured child will require the examiner to be concerned with classroom behavior, peer relations, behavior in the home, and in general, the nature of responses to significant people and situations in life.

If it is found that the child is emotionally disturbed, it is frequently recommended that he receive psychotherapy. Oddly, the myth still persists that organically impaired individuals cannot profit from psychotherapeutic intervention, despite the lack of support for this notion. This is especially unfortunate in light of the fact that handicapped children are frequently vulnerable to early frustration, which stems directly from their objective disability and which indicates that psychotherapy is clearly in order. Some of the difficulties in thinking and skills experienced by these children would undoubtedly show some improvement if attendant feelings of inadequacy and anxiety could be relieved. While it is not proposed that teachers be psychotherapists, they may certainly be psychotherapeutic in their sensitivity to and awareness of the child's feelings.

Educational Status

When the child is of school age, it is essential to evaluate his achievement level in basic school subjects. The report should include a description of his reading and calculating abilities. There is little doubt that the very existence of psychological deficits may have a lowering effect on the scores these children achieve. Because of this, the value of test scores is questioned by many. We may wonder what a reading score represents for a child with a perceptual problem. Is it a measure of reading ability or an indirect indication of perceptual disability? The answer to this is not wholly satisfactory. While perceptual ability is clearly involved in reading, it is equally clear that reading involves more than perceptual ability.

If a child has difficulty attaching number symbols to their concrete representations, we may wonder what his arithmetic score means. Is it a measure of calculating ability or an indirect indication of disability in symbolization? The answer, again, while not satisfactory, seems to be that symbolization is involved in calculating ability but the two are not equateable.

These crude conclusions regarding the relationship of disability and test score necessarily reflect adversely on the value of the achievement test as a proper index of ability in disabled children; these conclusions admit an unspecified role for perceptual and conceptual deficits in the determination of achievement scores. In effect, such questions as those presented above are concerned with the validity of tests for this population. One may also point to the fact that the normative samples for standard achievement tests do not include brain-injured children, and therefore any subsequent comparison of a brain-injured child's test results with these norms is questionable. As Birch has pointed out in his foreword to Haeussermann's book,[15] invidious comparisons between a specific handicapped child's test score and the norms for that test are often made on the assumption that the child has had experience with the required tasks or something like them at some time in his life. Such experience is literally precluded for some children because of the very nature of their handicap. It certainly seems likely that many brain-injured children are so handicapped. With these limitations in mind, it is possible to utilize achievement tests in a manner that is helpful in classroom programming. A statement of present functional status (and the implied comparison with normal children) provides the teacher with concrete "base lines" from which she can project future goals. These base lines are no less necessary as points of departure with brain-injured children than with normal children.

Evaluation Procedures

No attempt will be made in this section to describe the variety of psychological tests which are presently available and useful in the evaluation of brain-injured children. Lucid descriptions of such tests are available in Anastasi,[2] Allen,[1] Taylor,[26] and Buros,[9] and in the manuals that invariably accompany these tests.

The attempt will be made here to discuss how certain methods of testing may be brought to bear on the pertinent functions discussed in the preceding section. These methods of testing will be discussed in order to show how information beyond a test score can be obtained. Wherever possible, the relevance of this information for classroom procedures will be discussed.

Problems with Omnibus Tests

There are two kinds of tests that may be used to elicit information about cognitive functioning in children (1) the omnibus intelligence test which is composed of a variety of verbal and non-verbal tasks, and (2) the special test, which may be either verbal or non-verbal and which is usually confined to the measurement of a more restricted aspect of cognitive functioning. The various picture vocabulary tests are examples of the verbal special test.

Most of the problems which arise in the course of testing children with perceptual, language, or motor disorders are associated with the more complex omnibus tests. The omnibus test requires the child to respond precisely in those areas where he has a disability, and it is felt by many examiners that this imposes an unfair handicap on the child and misrepresents his intellectual status. Some examiners ask how one can feel justified in administering a task requiring motor coordination to a child with defective motor ability, or a verbal task to a child without speech?

There are other reservations about using such tests with special populations. The absence of brain-injured children from the standardization samples of well-known intelligence tests limits the use of their test norms for a given brain-injured child since these norms are accordingly not fully representative of the total population. This is the most frequent objection to the use of standard tests as indicators of intelligence in brain-injured children.

Insofar as intelligence test results are said to be predictive of future capacities to learn, they are, in that respect, dependent upon the internal consistency of the child. That is, it is assumed that the child will not suddenly lose or gain crucial abilities between earlier and later testings. Obviously, the occurrence of either loss or gain of basic ability would alter the predictive capacity of a test. It is possible that certain crucial gains characterize some points in the development of many brain-injured children. For example, the adolescence of these children is characterized by the emergence of increased capacities to attend and concentrate.

The course of development of intelligence itself and of basic cognitive abilities in these children is largely unknown and remains to be charted. If the predictive value of these tests is indeed limited for these children, it may be better to emphasize the test results as indicators of *current* achievement. But, even if we use intelligence test results only as indicators of what is presently available without implications for future functioning, there is often reason to wonder about the meanings of certain test findings. For example, there is evidence that an individual who is brain injured may be reordered in his hierarchy of responsiveness;[5] he will be responsive to different features of the environment than is the normal individual. As a result, cognitive responses that are functionally available for use may be dependent upon the way the task is structured — i.e. what there is to respond to. Altering the conditions of testing is, of course, not possible or appropriate with standard tests, and therefore frequently leaves unanswered the question: can the child perform this task under *any* conditions?

Hence, it is with reference to test administration and response interpretation that the examiner may feel uneasy. The following remarks are addressed to these problems and assume that despite all the difficulties of application, the omnibus test can play an important role in the understanding of the cognitive status of these children.

Concept of Adapted Testing

How are we to administer verbal tests to non-verbal children, or performance tests to physically handicapped children? One obvious solution is to administer only verbal tests to physically handicapped children and performance tests to language-handicapped children. This can be accomplished by the simple expedient of using either the verbal or the performance portion of the Wechsler Intelligence Scale for Children, or by resorting to one or more of the tests that are especially constructed for use with handicapped children.

There are many occasions when this approach may not be sufficient or even desirable. When handicap exists in either the motor or the language sphere, it is usually not total. That is, the more frequent clinical picture is one where language or motor ability is partially impaired rather than totally absent. When language ability is impaired, one would forego critical information about the level of language competence if a test involving only performance abilities were used. When there is motor impairment, a verbal test tells us nothing of performance abilities. There is value in observing a child with motor disability *trying* to complete a motor task, and there is value in observing a child with verbal disabilities *trying* to express an idea. Qualitative observations can be made of the child's approach to the task, his reaction to failure, his frustration tolerance, his interest, attention and interpersonal responsiveness. Such observations are as essential to a thorough evaluation as the simple fact of success or failure. If we proceed from the view that a variety of qualitative observations can emerge from a consideration of failures as well as successful performances, then it becomes logically necessary to observe the child performing tasks outside the range of his competence.

Consider the Stanford-Binet item "Copying a Bead Chain from Memory." The child is required to string beads of various shapes onto a shoe string in a given sequence after a model has been removed from view. Many psychological processes appear to be involved: visual discrimination, non-verbal memory, fine finger dexterity, visual-motor integration, attention and concentration. When a child fails a complex item like this, is it because of incompetence in all of these areas? This is, of course, possible but it is more likely that this is not the case. Deficiency in any one of these processes would be enough to produce failure. Observation of behavior on this task may provide the examiner with clues as to which of these processes is the source of major difficulty. We may hypothesize, for example, that poor finger dexterity alone prevents success on the item. To test this, the child might be asked to place the beads on the table in the prescribed sequence without using the shoe string. If he succeeds on this task, our hypothesis gains support and finger dexterity is implicated. If he fails, we will continue to wonder what processes are involved in the failure and will consider other ways in which to present the task. Perhaps the executive process of visual-motor integration is defective. To test this, the examiner may offer to perform the stringing, with the child directing the choice and sequencing of the beads. If the child succeeds under these conditions, visual discrimination and non-verbal memory may be presumed to be intact, attention and concentration adequate, and visual-motor integration alone to be defective. This method constitutes a test adaptation. It is understood, of course, that the child cannot receive scoring credit for successes based on adapted items; the formal scoring remains based on the standardized administration.

It may be helpful to give other examples of adapted testing. It is common for clinicians who work with language-handicapped children to adapt the picture vocabulary subtest of the Stanford-Binet. The standard administration requires that the child supply names to a series of pictures of common objects. In order to receive credit for an item, he must articulate the word comprehensibly. But, what if the child, although able to identify a picture, is unable to say the word? This defect need not be interpreted as reflecting the lack of the concept. This is recognized in the technique of giving the child a multiple choice of answers, orally presented, from which he must choose the correct answer. For example, the examiner points to the picture of a dog and asks, "Is this a boy . . . a horse . . . a dog . . . a cat?" The child need only nod or indicate a *yes* at the appropriate point in the questioning. He need merely recognize the correct answer; he need not be able to say it.

Resort to multiple choice or recognition responses lends itself readily to test items requiring verbal responses. Word definitions, picture identifications, object identifications, and questions requiring one word answers all lend themselves readily to multiple-choice adaptations. Even the much-used memory-for-digits item can be adapted through use of a multiple-choice technique. After exposure to a verbal presentation of digits, the child is presented with cards on which are printed correct and incorrect digit sequences; his task in this adapted situation is to select the card with the correct sequence. Other tasks for which multiple choice or matching for recognition can be used as adaptations can be determined on brief reflection by the clinical examiner.

Adaptation of non-verbal items presents different and sometimes more difficult problems. This is because the cognitive-perceptual competences underlying most performance items are often obscure. Consider the much-used variations of the Kohs blocks. What can we infer about the perceptual adequacy of the person who fails to reproduce a given design? Does the picture in his mind not correspond to the design on the card? Or, does he see accurately but lack the executive capacity to make his hands do what his mind sees? This distinction suggests an adaptation. If the child fails to reproduce a design accurately, he may be shown a multiple choice of completed block models and asked to choose the model which matches the design card. If he succeeds, we may infer that although the executive capacity of perceptual-motor integration is impaired, he is able to discriminate or match accurately. If he fails, defective discrimination may be inferred, and the implications for classroom instruction may be more serious since simple matching is basic to so many teaching procedures.

The variety of performance materials available suggests that only through a consideration of the individual item and its unique characteristics can adaptations be formulated. In general, there exists the need to appreciate the multidimensionality of the item so that the significance of failure can be more fully understood. Certainly, the ingenuity of the individual examiner will play a role in the construction of adaptations. The findings that stem from a test adaptation may serve as a basis for further inquiry. One might inquire, for example, into the child's matching abilities by using a variety of content including two-dimensional and three-dimensional materials, abstract designs, and pictures of familiar objects. Such differentiation of psychological processes may be supplemented with information based on classroom experience. This specifying of strengths and weaknesses is a long-term process and may perhaps most profitably be a joint venture for the psychologist and the teacher.

Potential Competence

In general, performance based on adapted test items should not be seen as influencing the basic scores derived from the test. However, information based on adapted items can be used in conjunction with the formal test score. If all the adapted successes are scored parenthetically and summed, the result may be viewed

as reflecting an *as yet* undifferentiated group of psychological processes. In the absence of knowledge of accurate psychometric expressions of these underlying processes, it may be helpful to lump
all these performances together for the moment under the convenient fiction of "potential competence." This concept requires
elaboration. It is not used synonymously with the term "potential
intelligence." Clinically, the concept of potential test performance
is often contrasted with actual test performance, and the assumption is made that the child would perform more effectively if
various affective and social factors were improved. The influence
of affective or social factors on test performance is irrelevant to
the concept of potential competence. Instead, the focus is on the
complex psychological requirements of any given item. Most
psychometric tasks, as in the case of bead stringing discussed previously, involve a variety of underlying psychological processes.
Failure on a given task, then, need not reflect inadequacy in all
of these processes. The fact is that most psychometric items contain
multidimensional requirements that are psychologically irrelevant
to one another. Deficiency in one process may interfere with the
proper expression of another process because of the intertwining
of the task requirements.

Fine finger dexterity, for example, is clearly irrelevant to the
psychological process of visual discrimination, but if it is impaired,
it will interfere with the child's capacity to perform the Stanford-
Binet bead stringing item and make it appear that he is defective
in discrimination. Making similar distinctions for other test items
and obtaining subjective measures of these separate abilities are
the goals of adapted testing. The sum of these abilities represents
a pool of resources, of potential competence, which is not documented during the ordinary administration of an omnibus test
of intelligence.

The evaluation of potential competence clearly requires the
subjective determination of those various psychological processes
that underlie a given item. When a child fails an item, the examiner's task begins. He must analyze the item by identifying contributing processes. He must then devise appropriate adaptations
designed to get at these processes either separately, or at least in

smaller combinations than that complex combination which characterizes the original item.

EDUCATIONAL RELEVANCE

Such procedures will naturally introduce a quality of subjectivity somewhat short of the psychometric ideal, but the goal will not be inconsistent with the test constructionist's search for more atomistic items. Undoubtedly, the validity of such procedures will increase as a function of the clinical experience of the examiner. It must be emphasized that although such procedures represent a departure from the usual administration of test items, they in no way mitigate the use and interpretation of the test in its original format. They represent an additional and later step in the evaluation process, and are suggested out of concern for what is educationally relevant and useful.

Advances in our understanding of these brain-injured children remain to be translated into universally accepted teaching procedures. The subjective evaluation of underlying psychological processes may contribute concretely to the development of appropriate instructional procedures. It is doubtful that educators will continue for long to accept with equanimity such gross characterizations as *poor verbal ability,* or *perceptually inadequate* or *verbal superior to performance.* Clinical examiners will want to respond to such questions (now only faintly heard but destined to grow louder) as: "Which of the child's verbal abilities are poor?," and "The child's perception of *what* stimuli are inaccurate?" Underlying such specific questions is a more general question that concerns the teacher — what special instructional procedures may be used to raise the child's level of functioning? The development of special instructional procedures seems more likely to occur in response to psychological specificity than to generalization. For example, if the child's difficulty is visual-perceptual, the specifics of this difficulty may consist of the definition of the *kinds* of stimuli that elicit adequate or inadequate responses. A child may be adequate with three-dimensional objects and inadequate with two-dimensional drawings and pictures; he may succeed with color but will fail with black and white. Such specificity lends itself readily to the development of special instructional materials. Specific analyses certainly cannot come from tests as they are commonly administered, nor will they come automatically from the kind of clinical inference suggested here. Obviously, the need for tests to determine basic psychological processes is especially evident when the discussion turns to the educational relevance of psychological information. Adapted testing, despite its limitations of subjectivity, seems to be one way to start the process of clinically translating the psychological evaluation into educationally useful procedures.

Special Tests

Although it is preferable for special tests to be seen as supplementary, there are occasions when they become central because of the unfeasibility of administering either the Stanford-Binet or the Wechsler Intelligence Scale for Children. For a complete listing of verbal and non-verbal cognitive measures see Buros.[9] For a selective review of those tests especially helpful with deaf and hard-of-hearing children, see Levine.[18] For the reader who is interested in tests which attempt a detailed analysis of speech and language, referral is made to Osgood.[24] Taylor[26] and Burgemeister[8] discuss the clinical use of a variety of tests with neurologically impaired children, and Allen[1] discusses the evaluation of cerebral-palsied children.

Those tests most frequently mentioned include the Leiter International Performance Scale, Arthur Point Scale of Performance Tests, Nebraska Test of Learning Aptitude for Young Deaf Children, Ontario School Ability Examination, Columbia Mental Maturity Scale, Peabody Picture Vocabulary Test, Goodenough Draw-A-Man Test, Drever-Collins Performance Scale, Merrill-Palmer Scale of Mental Tests, and Randall's Island Performance Tests. All of these tests provide the examiner with an estimate of general intelligence. All of them can be administered with a minimum of verbal instructions. The use of pantomime is sufficient to convey the demands of the required tasks. The Nebraska, Drever-Collins, and Ontario tests have norms for deaf children thus providing the examiner with a special reference group when that is desirable. The Columbia and the Draw-a-Man Tests are especially valuable as quick screening devices but have the disadvantage of depending greatly on perceptual and perceptual-motor abilities so as to offer a biased estimate of intelligence in children with disabilities in these areas of function.

The Bender Visual-Motor Gestalt Test and the Benton Visual Retention Test are often included in test batteries as a means of documenting perceptual adequacies. Difficulties in objective scoring result in their being used most often clinically as qualitative indicators of perceptual problems. They are especially helpful when used as sources for confirmatory evidence in a battery which includes omnibus tests.

Problems With Projective Tests

In general, the same tests and procedures found helpful with intact children may be tried with brain-injured children. The difficulties that arise in testing will reflect the nature of the child's cognitive problems. So, for example, if the child has difficulties which prevent him from correctly perceiving ambiguous designs or pictures as exemplified in the Rorschach and the various thematic apperception tests, the examiner has to determine whether or not the test results permit interpretation on a dynamic level. How much does a response reflect neural damage, and how much does it reflect psychodynamic forces? When in doubt, the conservative approach is to utilize information from sources such as observation, dramatic play, and case history. When the child is not able to verbalize well, greater reliance must be placed on these additional sources of information. These methods are described in detail elsewhere.[18,28]

Other Sources of Information on Personality

It is most helpful for the examiner to observe the child in the classroom, at play, and in interpersonal interaction with his peers and teachers. It is especially enlightening to exchange information with the significant adults in his life and to hear their views of him. Teacher observations are especially important.

A myth that persists consists of the assumption that test information is more accurate than direct observation. Hence, when the psychological examiner and the teacher report apparently inconsistent findings, the teacher is all too ready to abandon her position. The reconciliation of apparently discrepant observations need not resolve itself into a reflection of a status hierarchy but rather should reflect the facts. For example, the child who is observed to be cooperative in the examining situation and later is observed to be uncooperative in the classroom may be exhibiting a need for individual attention which, when denied, results in disorganized or apparently uncooperative behavior. That is, *both* observations may be correct, requiring that collaborative effort be made to analyze the behavior at issue. Such information would serve to identify the circumstances in which different levels of cooperation are elicited, and would likely be more useful to the teacher than descriptive generalizations such as "cooperative."

Adults normally seen as significant in the lives of normal children are no less significant in the lives of brain-injured children. In fact, it is difficult to avoid the conclusion that parents and teachers may play an even greater role with them than with normal children because of their inferior capacity to benefit from informal life experience due to cognitive defect and their inevitably greater reliance on formal instruction. The mere fact that a teacher is more sensitive to the nature of the child's difficulties automatically sets her apart from most other adults in the child's environment and makes her (and formal instruction) especially important. Moreover, the difficulties that these children exhibit in adjusting to the ordinary stresses of life require a talent for patience, for teaching, and for love on the part of the parents that superimposes an additional strain on what is even, under normal circumstances, a demanding relationship. Hence, it seems likely that teacher-child and parent-child relationships play a more important role with the handicapped child than with the normal child.

If it is true that parent-child and teacher-child relationships assume a special importance in the lives of handicapped children, it follows that the evaluation of these children requires an intensive look at interpersonal areas. It should be stressed that such evaluations cannot be properly carried out in the consultation room alone; the examiner should observe the child in interaction with others. Such observations enable one to see the child in those activities which often form the basis for the judgments of teachers and parents, thereby providing an objective frame of reference within which the examiner can evaluate such judgments. An evaluation of teacher and parent judgments can play a helpful role in understanding the adjustments of the child by providing direct information about the subjective context within which he is adjusting. For example, it is not unusual for a parent to describe a child as "clumsy" when asked about physical manifestations, when, in fact, the child is not clumsy. If a parent thinks a child is clumsy, this subjective context is a real fact that the child responds to, and it must be considered in the evaluation of the child's emotional status. More often, the term "normal" will be applied by parents to their child's behavior when their own adjustments are characterized by denial. If the child is described as "normal" when he is not, this, again, is a subjective context within which the child is adjusting, and it must be considered in evaluating his emotional status.

It follows from the above that one cannot describe the quality of the child's adjustment without paying equal attention to the quality of the parental adjustment to the child. The problem with such a statement is, of course, that while accepted in principle, it is not yet a clinical routine. Psychologists in many settings are often inclined to leave the evaluation of parents to other disciplines.

Although frequently observed, little in depth is known about the handicapped child whose adjustment to life — to school, play, peers, — is excellent. Enough is known to be able to say that severity of condition has no predictive significance for emotional adjustment. What, then, does have predictive significance? It seems likely that relevant variables will be found in intrafamilial attitudes and values, and it is therefore suggested that evaluation of the emotional status of brain-injured children emphasize information in this area.

Educational Status

Despite the limitations of using achievement tests standardized on normal populations, these tests should be viewed as an essential part of the evaluation process since they are a major source of reliable information regarding achievement status in basic school subjects. Referral to Buros[9] will help in the decision as to which of the available tests are most appropriate for a child at a given functional level. Since the basic skills at all grade levels depend on reading and arithmetic, the tests chosen should include some measures of these abilities.

It is increasingly apparent that the skills of reading and arithmetic are complex functions, the subtleties of which are obscured when test results are reported in a single score. Therefore, tests like the Gates Basic Reading Tests, the Metropolitan Achievement Tests, and the Stanford Achievement Tests, which attempt to sub-categorize various aspects of reading and arithmetic, are worthy of special consideration. If a child's reading achievement is reported merely as "third grade," there still remains the task of determining his level of functioning in such areas as word recognition, comprehension of details, comprehension of major ideas, and ability to make inferences. Any test which attempts to analyze the process under consideration into meaningful categories will provide the examiner with concrete "bench marks" upon which he may base recommendations for instruction.

Obviously, the examiner cannot rely on test data alone to describe educational status, any more than he relies on test data alone to describe emotional status. There are many non-cognitive as well as cognitive factors that enter into a child's response to the learning experience that the objective examination cannot record. The teacher, in her interaction with the child, is a major source of such information. Here, again, is an opportunity for collaborative analysis to take place. During the course of such collaboration, the teacher and the psychological examiner can exchange hypotheses regarding the source of the child's difficulties. These hypotheses can serve as bases for instructional recommendations. For example, if it is believed that underlying the child's reading difficulty is a deficit in pattern recognition, an instructional program designed to enhance pattern recognition may be developed. The very process of evaluating the efficacy of such a program then becomes the basis for a new joint evaluation effort between the teacher and the psychological examiner. Thus, educational evaluation becomes not only a collaborative but also a continuing process based both on achievement test data and classroom instructional procedures.

SUMMARY

The problem of the psychological evaluation of brain-injured children has been discussed from the point of view of the need for documenting strengths and weaknesses. Areas of psychological functioning which have pertinence for the classroom were described. By utilizing the concepts of *adapted testing* and *potential competence,* an approach to the assessment of these pertinent functions was described.

REFERENCES

1. Allen, R. M., and Jefferson, T. W.: *Psychological Evaluation of the Cerebral-Palsied Person.* Springfield, Thomas, 1962.
2. Anastasi, Anne: *Psychological Testing.* New York, Macmillan, 1957.
3. **Birch, H. G.** (Ed.) : *Brain Damage in Children.* **Baltimore, Williams & Wilkins, 1964.**
4. Birch, H. G., and Demb, H.: The formation and extinction of conditioned reflexes in "brain-damaged" and mongoloid children. *J Nerv Ment Dis, 129:*162-9, 1959.
5. Birch, H. G., and Bortner, M.: Stimulus competition and category usage in normal children. *J Genet Psychol, 109:*195-204, 1966.
6. Blacketer-Simmonds, D. A.: An investigation into the supposed differences existing between mongols and other mentally defective subjects with regard to certain psychological traits. *J Ment Sci (London), 99:*702-19, 1953.
7. Bortner, M., and Birch, H. G.: Perceptual and perceptual-motor dissociation in cerebral-palsied children. *J Nerv Ment Dis, 134:*103-8, 1962.
8. Burgemeister, Bessie: *Psychological Techniques in Neurological Diagnosis.* New York, Harper, 1962.
9. Buros, O. K.: *Sixth Mental Measurements Yearbook.* Highland Park, Gryphon, 1965.

10. Clements, S. D.: Minimal Brain Dysfunction in Children. *U.S. Dept. of Health, Education and Welfare, Public Health Service Publication No. 1415,* 1966.

11. Critchley, M.: The phenomenon of tactile inattention with special reference to parietal lesions. *Brain, 72*:538-61, 1949.

12. Eisenberg, L.: Behavioral Manifestations of Cerebral Damage in Childhood. In H. G. Birch (Ed.) : *Brain Damage in Children,* Baltimore, Williams & Wilkins, 1964.

13. Gallagher, J. J.: *The Tutoring of Brain-injured Mentally Retarded Children.* Springfield, Thomas, 1960.

14. Goldstein, K., and Scheerer, M.: Abstract and concrete behavior: An experimental study with special tests. *Psychol Monogr, 53* (2) , Whole No. 239, 1941.

15. Haeussermann, Else: *Development Potential of Preschool Children.* New York, Grune, 1958.

16. Jackson, H.: *Selected Writings of Hughlings Jackson.* In J. Taylor (Ed.) New York, Basic Books, 1958.

17. Kennedy, C., and Ramirez, L. S.: Brain Damage as a Cause of Behavior Disturbance in Children. In H. G. Birch (Ed.) : *Brain Damage in Children.* Baltimore, Williams & Wilkins, 1964.

18. Levine, Edna S.: *The Psychology of Deafness: Techniques of Appraisal for Rehabilitation.* New York, Columbia, 1960.

19. Lowell, E. L., and Metfessel, N. S.: Experimental concept formation test for preschool deaf. *J Speech Hearing Dis, 26*:225-29, 1961.

20. McGaughran, L. S., and Moran, L. J.: Differences between schizophrenic and brain-damaged groups in conceptual aspects of object sorting. *J Abnorm Soc Psychol, 54*:44-59, 1957.

21. Milgram, N. A.: Preference for abstract vs. concrete word meanings in schizophrenic and brain-damaged patients. *J Clin Psychol, 15*:207-12, 1959.

22. Milgram, N. A., and Furth, H. G.: The influence of language on concept attainment in educable retarded children. *Amer J Ment Defic, 67*: 733-39, 1963.

23. Oleron, P.: Conceptual thinking of the deaf. *Amer Ann Deaf, 98*:304-10, 1953.

24. Osgood, C. E., and Miron, M. S. (Eds.) : *Approaches to the Study of Aphasia.* Urbana, U. of Ill., 1963.

25. Saarinen, P.: *Abstract and Concrete Thinking at Different Ages.* Helsinki, Finland, U. of Helsinki, 1961.

26. Taylor, Edith M.: *Psychological Appraisal of Children with Cerebral Defects.* Cambridge, Harvard, 1959.

27. Thomas, A.; Birch, H. G.; Chess, Stella; Hertzig, Margaret E., and Korn, S.: *Behavioral Individuality in Early Childhood.* New York, New York University Press, 1963.

28. Thorndike, R. L., and Hagen, Elizabeth: *Measurement & Evaluation in Psychology & Education.* New York, Wiley, 1961.
29. Vigotsky, L. S.: Thought in schizophrenia. *Arch Neurol Psychiat, 31:* 1063-77, 1934.
30. Wunsch, W. L.: Some characteristics of mongoloids evaluated in a clinic for children with retarded mental development. *Amer J Ment Defic, 62:*122-130, 1957.

IV

PSYCHIATRIC FACTORS

STELLA CHESS

THIS CHAPTER DEALS WITH the behavioral difficulties that may be presented by brain-injured children. It does not discuss practical educational procedures, but rather the behavioral manifestations that must be taken into account by teachers of brain-injured children.

When the psychiatrist is called in to make a diagnostic study, he must first determine the context of the request. Sometimes he is expected to provide an overall psychiatric evaluation of the child — like a physical checkup, let us say. This type of evaluation is hardest because the investigator is given no clue as to what the child has been thinking and how he has actually been functioning. Without such a clue, one cannot properly interpret the meaning of the child's responses, nor can one be sure which answers need further exploration.

The child's answers tend to be shaped by the structuring of the examiner's questions. As a result, if the examiner assumes he has identified a problem area and pursues it, he may be giving disproportionate emphasis to minor matters while he bypasses the child's most prominent concerns. If a child is asked something like "Tell me about school," the answer is usually a vague statement like "It's all right." This response to an open-ended question may be given by a child, whether or not he has problems. Now the examiner must make a selection of areas to explore, probing in the direction that he thinks fruitful. For example, he may start by trying to find out whether the child considers the teacher benign or malignant. The response to leading questions may or may not reveal a basic attitude. It may by chance merely reflect a classroom event of the day before, and thus may be quite unreliable as an indicator of the total relationship.

Where there is a focus for the psychiatric evaluation, it is somewhat easier. The examiner can then be surer that the specific

95

questions he asks or the specific areas he probes are charged with meaning, and that he has not arbitrarily assigned importance to them. If he has a report, for example, that a child has difficulty in peer relationships — is a sore loser and pulls out of any competitive endeavor — then he can begin to pose questions in this area. Similarly, in examining a child with behavioral aberrations, a focus of exploration is suggested when the available history of behavior or previous medical examinations arouse suspicion that some type of structural damage accounts for at least a portion of the child's behavior.

This reference to structural damage suggests a second basic consideration. In talking about a brain-injured child, one is not talking about an undifferentiated entity. There tends to be a stereotyped approach which automatically identifies the brain-injured child with a child who is in one degree or another hyperactive, distractible, emotionally labile, and short in attention span. This is, of course, one type of behavioral manifestation of brain-injury — perhaps the best known, because such behavior most obviously interferes with a teaching situation calling for a child who can sit still and sustain attention for a length of time that is average for the age group.

But the brain is a very complex organism, and there are many types of brain-injured children. Some are characterized by the specific area of the brain that is damaged. The defect may be one that is subtractive; that is, it causes minimized or absent function. It may be one that is additive; that is, it causes a hyperfunction or added action causing dysfunction. The defect may be disorganizing, as with perceptual distortion or disturbance in the integration of two perceptual functions. As a result of the overall brain injury, scattered minute areas of the brain may be destroyed or the connections between areas disrupted; the total number of brain cells may be cut down or the passage of impulses between them reduced. One may then have a child who can apparently function normally until one increases the number of tasks being asked of him sequentially or in a given period of time. Other children may be hyporeactive and need much repetition before they can really grasp a concept; still others may simply be delayed in their responses. Thus the brain-injured child is not a general-ized type, but a child with a specific kind of difficulty due to structural aberration in the brain (and it is necessary to define the difficulty in each individual case).

Now let me touch on the relationship of motivation to struc-ture, having indicated in a very general way my meaning for *structure*. We are speaking of a child whose structural organiza-tion is deviant from the range that we consider normal. Remem-ber that this covers a wide range of capacity for motility, expres-siveness, attention span, selectivity of interest, and perseverance. The child whose brain structure is different from normal, and whose functioning will therefore be outside this range, is never-theless a reactive human being. Therefore, the way in which his aberrant behavior manifests itself will be closely related to environment.

Consider, for example, the child who is aware that he cannot sustain his attention; he is unable to remember the direction which says, "Would you please open the closet, look on the top shelf on the left, and get the watering can; go out and fill it with water and then water the geraniums." Perhaps this message has been repeated several times. The child's teacher expresses irrita-tion because this sort of thing has been going on all term. The child has taken to whispering to the youngster seated next to him. He has begun to clown. At this point an observer may all too readily assume that the child's failure to follow the teacher's de-mand has nothing to do with a fundamental incapacity to do so, but has to do rather with negativism or some other motivational issue.

The child has been so successful in behaviorally covering over his feeling of helplessness that he has done himself a disservice. If the incapacity were clear, the very busy teacher would perhaps respond to the child's need for help. As it is, the teacher responds to the fact that the child is walking around with a container of milk on his head, or hitting the boy in front of him, or doing something that seems quite unrelated to the question of follow-ing instructions. What happens then is that the child is seen as a nuisance and sees himself as a nuisance. A motivational quality has been added because this child is a reactive human being, and this may obscure the existence of a basic structural problem. The fact of a direct behavioral manifestation of brain injury may not be recognized by someone who does not approach this child as a total diagnostic problem. Yet the total behavioral problem combines the direct behavioral symptoms of brain injury with the defensive set of actions against the circumstances, which the structural difficulty brings about.

Complete diagnosis is a complex assignment. When I say, "Who is it that asks the psychiatrist to do the diagnosis and what is the context of the request?" this is the sort of thing I have in mind: Have the problems come up in this and that specific situation, but not in several others? How does the situation that seems to bring fourth the behavioral problem differ from situations in which it is absent — for example, is the problem-producing situation one in which there are very many activities going on, whether in the classroom, recreation hall, or family gathering? If one could assemble such data before starting the diagnostic procedure, one would have some clues for exploration. Just to make life harder for both the diagnostician and the person trying to work with the child in the educational setting, behavioral manifestations not based on structural difficulty can, under certain circumstances, appear superficially identical with those that are based on structural difficulty. The anxious child who has intact brain function can also be distractible and withdrawn, can also be unable to manage a whole group of sequential directions, and can also become very flustered when pressures are put on him for competitive functioning. Simply describing those sets of circumstances in which the child functions poorly and those in which he functions better does not give one *the* answer; it merely gives one directions for further investigation.

Other factors may play a part in affecting the behavior of brain-injured children. Reactions are always colored by the wide variety of personality types. The child's determination to master a situation and his ability to work on remedial procedures, whether they relate to physical rehabilitation or educational rehabilitation, are not directly related to the degree of handicap. One severely handicapped child may make optimum use of the rehabilitative approach and minimize, to the extent that his structure will permit, the difficulties presented by his handicap. Another child with a much milder difficulty of the same type — one can only compare children with difficulties of the same type — may get quickly discouraged and be unable to sustain his efforts, so that he makes little response to the same well-planned rehabilitative effort.

The response of each child is affected by a host of issues. While the nature of the child's structural difficulty is important, he brings a good deal more to the situation. By and large, the child who has a talent in one area is going to be the child who reaches the top in that area, but there may be another child with an equal amount of talent who has done nothing with it. (This fact is true of normal children but is sometimes forgotten in relation to handicapped children.) It needs to be stressed that the individual child's capacities or incapacities must always be mapped out in terms of both the structure of injuries and the personality that is brought to the remedial and educational task.

The child's awareness of his incapacity and the sureness of his attempt to minimize it may depend upon several other factors. To take sample considerations, when did the incapacity occur? Was this child born with the given defect, or did the brain injury occur later? (How far along in the child's life the insult occurred will of course make a difference.) The time-onset approach has long been worked out in other fields — for example, with hearing defects. A child who is born without hearing has no measure of voice and speech; a child who loses his hearing before a certain age will have the same type of problem as the child born deaf; but the problem is quite different if deafness occurs after an age at which a certain amount of auditory experience has accrued. Similarly, the child who has experienced normal locomotion or a normal learning capacity before brain injury occurred — say through disease, accident, or an expanding lesion — presents a different educational problem from the child who was born handicapped.

The latter child has handicapped existence as his norm. Here one must deal with the whole question, from extent to which this child is attuned to dependency, to expectation of service in the area of the defect, as opposed to the child who has had the experience of not needing to be serviced. This may make a great deal of difference in the circumstances in which the child is operating. Once again, however, it should be emphasized that many a child who always has been quite helpless physically may have such independence of personality that he will plow through, even though he has not had the formative experiential background. Conversely, many a child who was formerly quite normal will have responded to the cataclysm by moving into dependence, so that there is a problem of orienting him again to independence. In any event, it is clear that the timing of the onset of the brain injury is a major issue that should be borne in mind when making an evaluation.

Another issue is the type and degree of handicap. The type of handicap need not be stated here in terms of specific medical diagnosis, but in terms of the child's functional difficulties, since this is the important thing to the child so far as his reaction is concerned. For example, three broad types of functional difficulties might give rise to three types of discouragement to a child trying to overcome his handicap. The child, whose central damage has resulted in athetosis, faces a situation in which what he attempts to do is distorted, and the distortion is increased by his efforts. Thus, if he is reaching for a pencil, let us say, the very movements — the athetoid movements — interfere with what he is doing. This is quite a different problem of functioning from that of the child who has a partial paralysis or weakness of musculature; what this child does is aimed true, and here it is a question of how much effort he must put into it. In turn, this differs from the problem of the child who has spastic paralysis. The latter's effort is in the context of both weakness and spasticity, but the direction of muscular response is more predictable in some ways than that faced by the child with athetosis. The spastic child eventually discovers which way the pull of the muscles will be when he moves into effort, and he may possibly learn to correct for it.

Again, the child who has muscular difficulty of the limbs is certainly facing a different type of communication problem from the child whose greatest difficulty is in the muscles that control speech. The effort to carry through a motoric task like writing, as opposed to speaking, may be less embarrassing and frustrating to a child because he can be allowed to write at his own pace with nobody standing to wait for his output. But the child, whose efforts to communicate orally are so distorted that he must repeat or can only speak very slowly, becomes vividly aware that the person listening is growing impatient; or there may be three other children pulling at the person who is listening, so that the urgency of time further interferes with the communication. It is difficult for even a patient listener to be completely at ease with such a child. As the child's distress mounts, one tries to supply him with words; the listener's anxiety to be helpful in turn communicates itself to the child, increasing his distress. In this byplay, the nature of the difficulty stated medically fails to cover the nature of the difficulty stated functionally.

The child with a convulsive disorder may be embarrassed by the commotion that he has caused; he may be afraid to go into certain situations, whereas he may move with ease in others where he feels that no one will react to the convulsion. Here again is a functioning difficulty that can be understood only in terms of time, place, and level of independence expected of the child. A youngster may behave normally in most situations but may need to be carefully supervised in others because of a history of recurrent episodes. Certain activities — for example, swimming or going alone on the subway — may bring an inhibition in ordinary functioning that will baffle people who see no other obvious difficulty in the child. The same child may have an irritable brain, which shows up between convulsion episodes in sharp, intense reactions that are structural but superficially appear as motivational and personality difficulties.

The child's degree of involvement in a particular type of functioning handicap can be assessed only by studying the individual child. It is not enough to characterize the problem as mild athetosis or mild quadriplegia; a medical term does not give a picture of the living, breathing child. One must remember that children with behavioral aberrations have been gaining their life experiences in a specific family context; they have been handled in certain ways. True, the family and environmental handling may in large part get its quality from the fact that a handicapped child is involved. Nevertheless, the family members are people with their own personalities, and not every family responds in the same way to every child with the same type and degree of handicap. Some family handling is extraordinarily positive, constructive, and well-planned. (This does not always bear a direct relationship to the amount of advice the family has received.) Some families have a spontaneous common-sense attitude that the child should not be babied; they tell him to go and get a glass of water, even if it takes a half hour, so that he can learn to feel independent. On the other hand, there are families that take the psychiatrist's suggestions and distort them in the service of individual guilt feelings and chagrin, so that their handling is a caricature of the advice. Other families handle the handicapped child remarkably well, but not the normal child; the very qualities they can bring in response to the handicapped child would be wrong for the normal child.

In response to the way he is handled, the handicapped child develops attitudes that become new, independent factors. A brief illustration follows: A girl of nine was an inpatient on a rehabilitative service. Before the rehabilitative work relevant to her handicap could be mobilized, it was necessary to tackle her responses to her life experiences. This youngster's mother had left the family and her whereabouts were unknown. The father moved into the picture every once in a while, but this was really a case of "out-of-sight is out-of-mind." The family had low economic means, and the father's approach to jobs was not very stable. He had placed the child in privately arranged foster homes but often didn't pay the foster mother. As a result, there had been a succession of homes in which the child had been treated in different ways. One couldn't be sure what her handling had really been because this youngster had apparently learned that complaining was the way to get sympathetic attention. Experiences on the ward indicated that her descriptions of handling in the foster homes were not necessarily accurate. She tried constantly to exploit those around her, demanding privileges, complaining, and manifesting dependence.

A student nurse assigned to the child gave the following description of her experiences. The child told the nurse that she needed help getting in and out of the bath and the nurse provided such help. Within a week, the child's requests for assistance had expanded considerably. The nurse found herself virtually lifting the youngster in and out of the tub, scrubbing her from top to toe, and running all sorts of errands for her. Becoming aware that the child had gradually added to her helplessness, the nurse said to her, "But you know you can do this yourself, and I won't help you." Suddenly the child was doing the task herself and was back to the point at which she had started.

To understand this child's behavior, one must review the nature of the handicap. It had been present at birth. With proper braces and crutches, the child could walk, and she had no speech defects. Although her intelligence was dull normal, she was not retarded. She was not learning in school to capacity. Her manifestations of brain injury seemed to be almost entirely motoric. The behavioral issue here, then, was judged reactive and motivational, not primarily structural. One could surmise that identical behavioral habit patterns might have developed had this child not been handicapped but handled exactly the same way.

The first thing that had to be dealt with was the behavioral disorder, which was the response to a way of handling. It was not until this had been altered to a significant degree that one could begin really to estimate whether a remaining core of deviation of behavior was directly due to the brain injury and also determine what was needed for both physical and educational rehabilitation. The psychotherapeutic problem in this child's case had to do with her dependence and her tendency to exploit the environment. In the end, with the attainment of increased independence of functioning, she got constructive attention from the educational gains she made, and eventually her educational gains were commensurate with her mental age.

It must always be borne in mind, then, that brain-injured children are human beings with hopes and fears and reactive capacities. This adds all sorts of complications to the assessment of what is needed for the education of such children. Moreover, the handicapped child is not immune to the whole range of psychiatric difficulties that might develop were he not handicapped.

The following is a brief schema of psychiatric difficulties that could arise in brain-injured as well as in nonhandicapped children. First in the schema is the concept of *normal*. A child with brain injury may have no psychiatric disorder. His behavioral aberrations may be motoric only, and his psychological functioning may represent a healthy adjustment to his circumstances.

Next in the schema would be the reactive behavior disorders. These are behavioral aberrations which may seem inappropriate (that is, inconvenient) in normal situations, but are actually appropriate reactions to stressful situations. The stress may or may not be related to the fact of physical handicap. Consider, for example, a child who has been bitten by a dog. Even a normal child will get panicky in any situation that recalls the traumatic experience. To a physically handicapped child, the identical situation may have additional elements of trauma. Yet with both children, the behavioral manifestations — if seen out of context or without knowledge of the episode — may not appear related to the trauma, unless scrutinized. In the same way, a child's reactions of sensitivity to certain handling, say by a teacher, may prove to be related to poor parental handling. The child's reactive behavioral disturbance is quite logical and pertinent, even though at times it does not seem completely appropriate to the presenting situation.

Fixed, rigid, inappropriate behavior would fall under the next category — neurotic behavior disorders, in which traumatic events such as repeated shifts of domicile, pile up so quickly that the child has no chance to recover from individual episodes. Under these circumstances, a child may develop neurotic apprehensions of disaster, or he may acquire exploitative or dependent attitudes.

Once a neurotic attitude has been formed, ordinary occurrences can act as reinforcement. A child who is sensitive to competitiveness may begin to feel that every competitive situation is one in which he is being stepped on. If the child, feeling that everybody is trying to take advantage of him, develops an irritability and a "chip-on-the-shoulder" attitude, this view of the world will seem justified by the actions of many people he meets. The handicapped child is vulnerable to a variety of neurotic attitudes that may be originally engendered by a series of fortuitous events or by noxious daily handling. These attitudes are then kept going by the environment's response to the way this child reacts.

A further category in the schema is the concept of *psychopathic personality*. This refers to those children whose capacity to form meaningful interpersonal relationships has never developed — possibly because they have lacked early experience with close human relationships, because they have been institutionally reared from infancy, or because they have been moved about so much that they have not formed identifications with a specific group.

Such problems may appear among brain-injured children who are hospitalized in infancy and institutionally reared. A diluted version of this problem is commonly presented by children who have had long periods of hospitalization after the infancy period and who have become too thoroughly adjusted to ward routine with its shifting personnel. They become ward gossips and complainers; they hang on to anyone, and the relationship has no real depth and meaning, rather it is directed toward getting more attention. A child's personality may become so distorted as a result of long periods of hospitalization that he really cannot fit into a family setting even though he is not a true psychopath. In addition, long hospitalization may mean that the family setting becomes organized without the child, and he may even lose his bed, a symbol of his having a place at home.

The next two categories are probably the ones most pertinent to differential diagnosis. These are the psychotic or schizophrenic child, and the mentally retarded child. Much controversy has been aroused over the use of the term *psychotic* for schizophrenic children. Behaviorally, the socially adjusting schizophrenic child is quite different from the same child in a state of confusion, acute disorganization, and inability to test reality at age level. Agreement as to the proper definition and subclassifications of childhood schizophrenia leaves much to be desired. The basic disagreement pertains to the conceptualization of the child's schizophrenic adjustment as (1) based on organic brain damage, and (2) functional with no definable or diagnosable brain damage. At the present stage of our knowledge, some of the typical schizophrenic pictures seem to have indications of organic damage, whereas some do not.

Mental retardation is not in itself a pure diagnosis. Children who function at a mentally retarded level may have organic brain injury that shows up in physical defect as well as in cognitive defect. Mentally retarded children may also behave in a confused manner, and it is often difficult to know whether the retarded functioning is due to basic confusion or whether the confusion stems from retarded functioning in an environment that makes inappropriate demands for comprehension. By definition, a child whose brain structure makes him incapable of normal intellectual functioning is brain injured. The tendency, however, from the point of view of planning and special educational needs, is to differentiate between the child whose brain injury is expressed only in slowness of cognition and the child whose brain injury is expressed through the other symptoms discussed above.

In addition, those children, whose primary diagnosis is schizophrenia in a form which is at present untreatable, may need to be handled for optimum management in terms of their functional intellectual retardation. The main differentiating factor in some of these cases would relate to the child's response to repetitive and oversimplified learning procedures in which elements of a more complex organizational and conceptual kind are introduced only gradually. While this learning approach may be appropriate for both the retarded child and the schizophrenic child who functions as a retardate, one may find a differential response in the long run. The retarded child will be limited by his conceptual ceiling; some schizophrenic children, once their confusion is overcome by the rote approach, are capable of moving on to higher conceptual levels than had previously been suspected. In a sense, even the compulsiveness and perseverance of some schizophrenic children may be utilized in teaching them both formal lessons and rules of social behavior. However, it is dangerous to assume that an occasional flash of functioning, which seems to be at a higher cognitive level in either a mentally retarded child or a confused schizophrenic child, indicates a potential to function evenly at that level. Characteristic of brain-injured as well as schizophrenic children is their uneven functioning, and their shifting capacity for attention and concentration. Consequently, for adequate planning and basic orientation of the educational program, it is improper to set the goals either at the lowest level of functioning or at the highest level of functioning. The goals set must take into account this fact of uneven functioning and, therefore, the need for constant reassessment of the child's capacity.

Mentally retarded children, brain-injured children, and schizophrenic children are not immune to being hurt by inappropriate handling, and the chances are that they will have many more traumatic experiences than the average child. Thus, they may develop compulsions, anxieties, and habit patterns of bizarre quality as defensive maneuvers. In addition, any child's behavior which deviates considerably from age expectation is likely to look bizarre because observers automatically take their expectations from physical appearance and are disoriented by a discrepancy of behavior and age.

In summary, a description of the behavior of brain-injured children must note a number of psychiatric factors which teachers have to utilize in planning optimum educational approaches. The identification of the structural damage of the brain-injured child requires consideration of the extent and pattern of injury to the brain. Some of the behavioral symptoms encountered in the classroom are direct, primary representations of the brain injury. A further source of behavioral aberration has to do with secondary defensive reactions. These express either the child's anxiety about his malfunctioning or his distorted attempts to master it. Such efforts at mastery may range from merely inappropriate and ill-designed devices, through denial, to active behavioral interferences with the educational endeavor. In addition, the behavior is complicated by the quality of distortion in functioning as well as the time in the child's life when this malfunctioning arose. Finally, there is the question of the temperamental attributes of the brain-injured child. These attributes, independent of the brain injury itself, influence the child's behavior in the classroom situation. A diagnostic schema for categorization of these children is described and the criteria for the individual categories given.

REFERENCES

1. Birch, H. G., and Lee, J.: Cortical inhibition in expressive aphasia. *Arch Neurol Psychiat, 74:*514-7, 1955.
2. Bortner, M., and Birch, H. G.: Perceptual and perceptual-motor dissociation in cerebral-palsied children. *J Nerv Ment Dis, 134:*103-8, 1962.
3. Birch, H. G. (Ed.): *Brain Damage in Children — The Biological and Social Aspects.* Baltimore, Williams & Wilkins, 1964.
4. Chess, S.: *An Introduction to Child Psychiatry.* New York, Grune, 1959.
5. Chess, S.: Psychiatric treatment of the mentally retarded child with behavior problems. *Amer J Orthopsychiat, 32* (5):863-9, 1962.
6. Laufer, M. W., and Denhoff, E.: Hyperkinetic behavior syndrome in children, *J Pediat, 50:*463-74, 1957.
7. Money, J. (Ed.): *Reading Disability: Progress and Research Needs in Dyslexia.* Baltimore, Johns Hopkins, 1962.
8. Pasamanick, B., and Knobloch, H.: Brain damage and reproductive causality. *Amer J Orthopsychiat, 30:*299-305, 1960.
9. Strauss, A. A., and Lehtinen, L.: *Psychopathology and Education of the Brain Injured Child.* New York, Grune, 1947.

V

NEUROLOGICAL CONSIDERATIONS

WILLIAM R. BONIFACE

Charge

JOHNNY WAS THE CENTER of attention. He had been since he had first climbed to his feet and changed from a pleasant baby to a disorganizing principle in his parents' lives. They had hoped for the day when school would take him in tow; but now school protested that he was unmanageable in a classroom and requested he not come. Despairing, his parents took him to a doctor.

By all usual standards, Johnny was healthy and strong, normally intelligent, and well-coordinated. He was lively and attractive. He was too lively; he could not sit still, pay attention consistently, or be confined within any working discipline. Perhaps, the doctor wondered, Johnny was unable to contain himself because his brain was damaged. Perhaps, because he did not present the usual evidence for brain damage, Johnny was showing effects of some "minimal brain damage."

Determination of brain damage should seem a fairly simple matter, and so it would be, if we could look at brains as directly as we do scraped knees and estimate the nature and extent of damage. However, the evidence is not open to simple inspection, and its interpretation is complicated by our incomplete appreciation of the brain's complexity and the considerable limitations of the observations which are open to us. In such a case, it is usual to call in the neurological expert, but it is frustrating to find how often he has little to add, especially in the evaluation of "minimal" brain damage. Opinion and surmise are, of course, available, but these appear as a shrug of the shoulders, with qualifications.

Eyewitness

There are situations in which brain damage may be clearly delineated. When unfortunate circumstance allows direct study of brain tissue, unequivocal statement is possible, usually too late.

We do not come upon brain tissue casually, for we cannot sample it for study as we might sample other tissues like muscle, kidney, and liver — small bits of which can be obtained fairly easily with the assurance that the body can get along without or replace what we take. Such a small bit or *biopsy* of brain can be excised too, but uneasily and after the patient's state is past interest of educator or psychologist. Again, unique properties of the brain conspire to limit us. Biopsy generally is limited by the possibility that the sample does not present abnormalities, but other tissue left inside does, and such "sampling error" is also a problem in brain biopsy. Since one piece of muscle, kidney, or liver is much like another, we have assurance that our sample is representative of the organ under study. However, nervous tissue is notable for the extreme specialization of its parts, and in some particulars a biopsy would be characteristic only of the sample itself. In addition, nervous tissue has limited capacity for repair, and the functionally active components, the nerve cells, have virtually none. To consider brain biopsy then is to court some risk for possibly small reward, unless one is considering generalized disease in a brain already seriously deranged. I have not considered technical problems which further restrict this approach.

Post-mortem examination may offer the entire nervous system for study and make the matter of brain damage as open to decision as we now are able to effect, yet there is one further consideration. I have approached "brain damage" as an anatomical problem and have mentioned anatomical methods. This is the only setting in which the term has unequivocal meaning; however, the primarily anatomic approach has severe deficiencies. Anatomy is not function, and individuals become objects of concern for parents, schools, authorities, physicians by reason of how they function or behave, and not for some hidden anatomical peculiarity. Interpretations of aberrant behavior as consequent to brain damage require some assurance in the correlation of form and function, and such assurance rationally should be restrained within the opportunities to see form in action by the methods of observation open to us.

Our slight opportunity to see the form of the nervous system in many examples of unusual behavior has secondary effects which add to the difficulty. When we do have direct observation of brain, we often do not have the background to base problematic behavior on what we see. Uncertainty as to proper interpretation of an abnormal biopsy specimen makes it even less likely that biopsy be attempted — and so forth circularly to the preservation of our ignorance.

I have at this early point belabored the necessity, inadequacies, and frustrations of the anatomic manner of understanding in order to put it aside and focus on the nature of neurology and what to expect of it. What does a neurologic evaluation imply? Why is the result considered arguable in the instance of "minimal brain damage," when neurologists may be astutely discerning in, say, diagnosing a brain tumor on evidence much less apparent to the lay observer? The argument thus far is that a diagnosis of "brain damage" depends on anatomic demonstration as its final support. Such support is seldom sought in life, nor are we likely to increase our efforts in this direction soon. Since neurologists are willing to offer opinions despite these concerns, we must use indirect evidence and reasoning to attempt understanding. Indirect methods generally are more subtle and complex, more widely useful, and less reliable than the direct — and neurology is no exception.

Circumstantial Evidence

The possible error in indirect reasoning is that it is contingent; if we see *this,* then *that* which we don't see must occur. So long as there is only one inferred possibility, we are on firm ground. If I see the shadow to the right of a tree but do not see the sun, I expect the sun nevertheless to be on the left. When several influences may be operating together irregularly or at odds one with another, caution is needed. A photograph of a tree with the shadow to the right may suggest that (1) the sun was on the left; or (2) the sun was on the right, but the picture was printed with the negative reversed. More far-fetched possibilities include no sun at all but artifical lighting, no tree at all but a small plant against misleading perspective, or an artful retouch. We can deal with our confusion by guessing (sometimes brilliant and often wrong), by estimation (guessing biased by statistics), by simplification (ignoring some possibilities), by analogy (possibly misleading), and by vacillation (reliably useless). All of these methods and likely more have been attempted toward resolution of the neurologic puzzle.

Diagnostic thinking by neurologists is indirect because our observations bear indirectly on our concerns. We do not usually see damaged and disturbed nervous systems, but rather we note aspects of behavior and appearance which we interpret as reflecting the condition of the nervous system. Development of neurology as a discipline has been carried on largely by discerning amid the complex and continuous experience of encountering a patient, isolated items and aspects which we have learned demonstrate fairly directly the function of some component of the nervous system. A neurologist examining a patient does many odd things, one of which — tapping knees — is probably permanently in the comedian's repertoire. The neurologist also asks the patient to do many odd things, like touch forefinger to nose with eyes closed. After a series of such charades, the doctor then pronounces on the state of the unseen, often seeming rather like a soothsayer or stage magician. Like odd behavior generally, much of this strangeness evaporates if its rationale be known. Because the neurologist's professionally qualified opinion is based largely on this sort of examination, it might be useful to single out a few of the things he does and to ask what basis he has for interpreting them.

A neurologist's examining kit contains an odd assortment of junk: pins, the little rubber hammer, a flashlight, sometimes dry coffee in a little vial, a tuning fork, ticklers and scratchers, and a tape measure. His only usual doctor's equipment may be tongue depressors, a stethoscope, a blood pressure cuff, and a little round-headed light with which he gets uncomfortably close and peers inscrutably into eyes. The stethoscope he disconcertingly applies to head and neck. Much of the time, he ignores this pack of toys and puts the patient through a series of contortions and postures. In a pinch, he can do without most of the equipment except the ophthalmoscope — the round-headed light for eye-gazing. The only indispensable instruments are his own eyes, ears, and other senses, well-open, and his own nervous system. As in other things, it does no harm if he also has imagination.

Simplest of all to understand is what he does with the ticklers and scratchers, the feathers and pins. He tickles and scratches, asking what is felt and where. The tuning fork and warm or cool objects may be put to similar use. He wiggles the patient's toes, held between thumb and forefinger, and asks monotonously, "What do you feel?" The patient by instruction nods, speaks, gestures, or perhaps remains unresponsive. This homey sequence is already rather complicated. A physicist would say that the doctor was bringing energy in various forms to bear upon the patient's surface; some distant part of the patient, like the speaking apparatus, then moves. Again from a physicist's point of view, how was the energy transmitted and magnified to produce effects at some remove from, and so much greater than, the original amount applied? Further, the energy was not only transmitted and amplified, but also it provoked a specific and patterned response encouraged by prior instructions for the patient to say *Yes* or to nod; the response was *programmed,* as designers and users of computers have taught us to say. How such programming was set by means of a few vocal sound waves is another mystery. Of course, even without instruction we can note that some return for energy invested is usually delivered; stepping on a cat's tail induces a fairly reliable response even without instruction to the cat, and sticking people with pins without first telling them why may be similarly dramatic. Even as the patient is saying *Yes,* that he feels it, he may wince or start and indicate by tone of voice how he feels about the procedure he is being subjected to. To avoid the kind of confusion that derives from the diverse concerns described above, the trained physician studies one aspect at a time.

Exhibit A

The simplest aspect, to begin, is the transmission of energy. Here, too, there are mysteries. The scratch should stop at the skin surface; what goes on beneath must be energy in another form.

How it was converted to or produced in new form from the scratch might be questioned. In which form is energy transmitted? While these both are important questions toward which active investigation is directed, there is little question about the structures involved in transmission from the site stimulated. Ramifying throughout the body from the spinal cord are fibrous bundles, the nerves, branching finely into twigs which end in virtually every structure. Severing one of these deprives the structure in which it ends of sensation and/or movement. When, after stimulus, there is response, the nerve fibers transmitting the information are demonstrated as intact, and the neurologist's ticklings and pokings enable him to assay the intactness of these nerves and their component fibers by noting what is felt and where. Also, from movement and other activity, he notes further evidence bearing on the nerves; tissues deprived of nerve supply wither. Since there is slight opportunity for misinterpretation about the information on this level in the nervous system, as discerned in neurologic examination, there is little confusion about what happens in damage to what are called the peripheral nerves. Even though the injured nerve is not seen, its state can be rather confidently expected, like the location of the sun from the shadow under a tree.

Exhibit B

When a knee is tapped and the leg kicks out, we encounter a new order of complexity. So long as we restricted our attention to the mere facts of sensation or movement, we noted information useful for estimating the state of the peripheral nerves; but in regarding the tendon reflex at the knee, we have opportunity to wonder about the relation between tap and kick. To wonder effectively, we need to know more about the nervous system than has been mentioned. Our attention turns now to the spinal cord.

To define damage to the peripheral nerves requires mainly adequate knowledge of anatomy. The nerves are like cables which carry information and orders about the body. Knowing where they go and how they course is enough to guide understanding of most problems relating to injury of them; therefore, I am omitting many details useful in the actual evaluation of their function.

The spinal cord in some ways resembles a cable. It has a cylindrical shape, and there are bundles of fibers which traverse all or part of its length. Also, it is more. All of the nerves below the neck are spliced into it (a couple of exceptions here, but the details are not relevant to this discussion.) When peripheral nerves are cut, movement, sensation, and all reflex responses are eliminated in some area. When the spinal cord is cut across, separating part of it from the brain above, many complex changes occur in the part of body served by the isolated cord segment and the nerves which tie into it; however, reflexes such as the knee jerk may be preserved. The neurologist taps the knee and the leg kicks out. The kick informs him that between the nerve fiber, which transmits the news of the tap, and that which orders a muscle to shorten, a segment of the spinal cord is working.

Definition of a few terms may help here. *Stimulus* means simply *goad;* when we stimulate someone, we are goading him into action. *Response* is familiar, as is its synonym, *answer,* which originally apparently meant *swearing back,* a fitting retort for being goaded. *Reflex* we know better as *reflection,* and the metaphor pictures the response as an altered form of the stimulus reflected back to us: an automatic kind of reflection such as mirrors provide. A *reflex response* then is automatic and does not require the cooperation of the patient beyond his allowing examination either actively by agreement or passively by indifference or unconsciousness. The features of the reflex response are determined by the structure and state of the nervous system. I have chosen to analyze the knee jerk since it is relatively simple and typical.

The knee jerk is only *relatively* simple. It requires integrity of the local nerves and their segment of spinal cord, even though these may be isolated from the rest of the nervous system. This is not to say that the response is uninfluenced by other parts of the nervous system. The patient may be instructed largely to inhibit it; if he is very anxious, it may be exaggerated (these two influences disappear after sufficient damage to the spinal cord). If the muscles producing movement about the knee are very lax following other damage to the nervous system (e.g., to the cerebellum), instead of stopping promptly, the shank may swing back and forth like a pendulum. The knee jerk may persist after spinal cord damage; it is not unaltered: initially, it may not be obtained; later, it may become and remain hyperactive. Clearly, the spinal cord must be an area of interconnection, unlike the peripheral nerves where parallel bundles of fibers lie side by side with no notable effect one on another. The outer aspect of the spinal cord consists of similar parallel strands, but a cut into it reveals an *H*-shaped core, rosy grey in color, in contrast to the creamy white about it. The two distinctive regions of the cord derive from characteristics of the nerve cell (s).

A nerve cell, like other cells, is a blob of jelly constrained by a membrane. It is a blob drawn out around the edge into processes of various length. One (or two) of these processes — perhaps insulated by fat — may be extremely long, may leave the neighborhood and, joining others like it, may extend to distant parts of the nervous system. The ultimate ends of these processes have no insulation and branch profusely. The tips rest on other nerve cells. In course, such a long process, or axon, may have had several branchings, similarly ending. If we look at nerve cells anywhere, we see them invested in the axon tips of other cells. Some axons leave the spinal cord to become the peripheral nerves. Shorter cell processes, called dendrites, extend among the neighboring cells and receive branches of their axons. Since the uninsulated cell bodies and smaller fibers are usually grey, whereas the fatty insulation is creamy white, the colors grossly evident in cross section of the spinal cord are explained by location of the parts named. Some of the tracts of fibers along the outside of the spinal cord come from cells below and course upward; some come from cells variously located above. Singly, on their way, fibers emerge from the bundles, penetrate the grey core, and end near several cells and their processes. The interconnectedness postulated from function is amply evident in structure.

To understand more than the mere existence of reflexes like the knee jerk, our attention is directed above the spinal cord to the vast bulk of the nervous system. So far, the knee jerk may be absent because of damage to peripheral nerves, because of damage locally to the spinal cord, because of acute damage higher in the spinal cord, or because of willed suppression. If it is present, the knee jerk proclaims the function of the local spinal cord segment. When we attend to the degrees of activity as well, we find ourselves beginning to consider the brain. The number of explanations for the same observation has increased greatly, and we have only begun. A practicing neurologist would test many functions not detailed here and would usually be able to arrive at an appropriate understanding of where damage may have occurred to a patient's nervous system; but confronted with an isolated response like a knee jerk, he can only speculate. The complexity of the central nervous system is manifest in possibilities rather than categories.

Exhibit C

When the examining neurologist scratches about the foot, he is interested in response in the great toe, in which way it moves. If it moves down or perhaps does not move, he usually proceeds to other considerations; if it should go up, he becomes more inquisitive. Although he is looking at a toe, he is thinking of many things, including the cerebral cortex. Filling the skull like a fat walnut, the cerebrum is ninety per cent of the body's nervous tissue and is what most of us think of as brain. It is usually regarded as our most distinctly human structure (a good argument could be mustered for hips and feet). Yet it is involved in reflex response of the toes.

When we wish to move our toes, we simply wiggle them. Removing a certain portion of the cerebral surface, or *cortex* (which means *bark*), results in considerable impairment in this capacity. Extending from this portion of the cortex, the *motor strip,* to various levels in the spinal cord is a bundle of fibers known as the *corticospinal tract,* named like some railways for the two ends of the line. Interruption of the corticospinal tract is profoundly disabling to a human being, similar to removing the motor strip of cortex, since the tract brings the influence of the cortex to bear upon the spinal cord. As the neurologist scratches the foot and watches the toe, he thinks of tract and area of cortex, for he usually interprets rising of the toe as interruption somewhere in them.

By now we have learned not to be dogmatic: arthritic stiff joints may not move, and disability of muscle or nerve may interfere with our capacity to observe reflex response. A competent physician would first have checked for these. In sleep, coma, and infants, the toe may go up without this response being a sign of damage. The whole matter would be of slight significance except that in its path, from cortex to lower cord serving the lower extremities, the tract has traversed most of the length of the nervous system. As with telephones that do not work, once we have determined that the instrument itself is not damaged, we go tracing along the line to see what has happened. Many other bands of fibers exist in the nervous system, and we have learned to infer damage to some of them from other detectable differences in what we observe by examination. In their sum, they are not the whole nervous system, but they go through, near, or around many other structures. The integrity of the tracts and the normality of the functions they influence tell us that nothing is likely to be grossly wrong with large parts of the nervous system.

Expert Witness

It is possible to go on and develop many other units of the neurologic examination, but I am not writing a manual. Although I have referred to anatomy and function of the nervous system, I am not writing primarily on them. I am writing on the thoughts of a neurologist as he examines a patient, and these thoughts have concerned *damage* throughout — instead of damage, *abnormality* might do.

In any case, a neurologist certainly is not qualified by his examination to speak of brain function. Behind complicated associations like those above, lie the attitude of a physician and his awareness of why people come or are brought to him. Something is wrong; the physician is expected to do what he can to make it right. Behind him, his own experience and that of others have trained him to recognize signs of trouble when he meets them. In attending to the toe as it rises, his interpretations are based on no sure acquaintance of what the corticospinal tract does. He must rely on the experience that after damage to the tract or related cortex, the toe may move thus; he must lean on the knowledge that damage to either part has been found on many occasions when there has been opportunity to look. The movement of the toe is trivial and meaningless except against this background.

As he conducts an examination, a neurologist is much like a mechanic who knows the model of engine he is working with and listens for the pings and gratings. Before the signs to which the physician is so alert were validated, someone looked at an abnormal brain (or spinal cord or nerve) and saw where it was damaged. His picture of that damage underlies his alertness. Diagnoses are then formulated on the signs alone, and the fact the neurologist may not personally see damaged tissue is almost unnoticed in his assurance.

How well does this approach serve a neurologist? In his usual role, it serves very well. By various signs, he is able to check many parts of the nervous system. The parts he knows to check are near others, and most damage of any extent is likely to involve something he can detect. Brain tumors are noted since eventually they grow into tracts which warn him, like burglars tripping alarms. Many of the capacities tested, like ability to feel the position of one's limbs and to move, are important in themselves. It is necessary that deficit in them be accounted for.

These checks are by no means all that a neurologist relies upon. He knows more than he understands, and some situations are recognized, like friends, by appearance and not by knowledge of how they got that way; thus problems like seizures are diagnosed and treated without evident signs of damage. In general, in problems of sufficient extent, in progressive illness, and on familiar ground, a neurologist's skills are helpful. It remains to examine how he functions in unfamiliar situations, without known landmarks, such as we encounter in the "minimally brain-damaged" child. Without further definition for the moment, I shall refer to "minimally brain-damaged" children as presenting no usually recognized neurologic abnormality; but stirring concern in those responsible for these children leads to evaluation by a neurologist.

Certainly, if someone is thought to have brain damage of any degree, neurologic examination is indicated. Unusual findings can be evaluated as suggested above without calling the method into question. If nothing unusual is noted on examination, at least we are not likely to misinterpret. It is familiar to encounter problems where nothing is awry — yet. Watchful waiting will do no harm. However, on many examinations, responses are noted which, though not clearly abnormal, are not quite normal. Other responses, clearly abnormal, may have no established background as the result of a known variety of nervous tissue damage. Sometimes brain damage, not manifest by signs evident at time of examination, is inferred from injury definitely or likely incurred in the past — such as an episode of encephalitis or a difficult delivery after which the infant was slow to respond. A rather slow development may raise question of whether it results from an abnormal nervous system. On a purely descriptive level, we are considering an uneven group, more characterized by our ignorance than by any common features.

Till now, I have not directly noted how *concrete* neurologic thinking is. In the dialogue of form and function, form has won out, and behavior tends to be thought of in terms of structure. At first blush, experience supports this view. Sensation and movement find partial materialization in sense organs, nerves, and muscles. The sequential observation called the knee jerk takes form in connections in the spinal cord. Voluntary movement has substance in the "motor strip" of the cortex and corticospinal tract. When these structures are disrupted, the behavior concerned is disturbed. It seems only the next step to say that disturbed behavior means abnormal structure in whatever part of the nervous system mediates that behavior. On encountering a child who behaves abnormally, one is already predisposed to find something abnormal with his nervous system. If he presents no known neurologic sign, one merely files the report against the day when someone discovers the structural abnormality responsible. Perhaps this approach is correct, and time will answer our questions as it has many others. It is easy to overlook that the statements above are oversimplified and deceptive.

A responsible neurologist will quickly assert that there is certainly more to sensation, movement, reflexes, voluntary movement than the structures named; he will support the statement by adding many more structures and their relationships to each function. He can tell you how to detect disturbance in these additional structures. Still, no matter how far we carry this process, the list of functions covered does not begin to be a description of behavior, through it is an excellent guide for trouble shooters. It is an attitude of faith to expect this approach to answer all questions.

An aspect of concrete neurologic thinking is that damage to the nervous system is thought of as damage to specific structures in definite locations. To speak of brain damage and its consequences without localization runs counter to this tendency and counter to one of the neurologist's strongest urges, to diagnose treatable conditions promptly. The poor capacity for repair of nervous tissue drives him to do so before damage becomes possibly more widespread and more disabling. The concrete, structure-oriented, limiting and localizing aspects of neurologic thought are adapted directly to this end and are in the patient's best interests. Thus a neurologist is biased to view aberrant behavior — considered professionally — as evidence of brain abnormality, and he finds this idea uncomfortably vague unless he can specify the abnormal structures in each instance. The way out would seem to be more intensive effort to localize, but we are considering a group of patients upon whom such effort has been unproductive, so far.

Objection

Part of the conflict arises from a misstatement of the problem, deriving from a fallacy I have allowed to go unchecked from almost my first remarks. When first I mentioned correlating form and function, I did not define my terms. Later, when I said form had won out over function, I did not indicate that the distinction between form and function is inappropriate in referring to the nervous system and behavior, and that *correlation* is the significant term — correlation not of structures and actions but of observations made under varying circumstances over a period of time.

The observations which we make have various attributes, some ephemeral, others more lasting. As we contemplate the knee jerk, the sequence "thigh-knee-shank" is fairly constant while the angle at the knee changes. We then tend to call the "thigh-knee-shank" sequence, *structure* (form), and to call the varying angle, *function*. After noting the reproducibility of the knee jerk, we recall the nerves, spinal cord, et cetera, and speak of the knee jerk as a *function* of these *structures* (forms). We usually do not see the nerves or central nervous system of a patient; we expect these by analogy with nervous systems in others, as in experimental animals; yet we accord to them a substance that we do not give the knee jerk, which we did see. By *form* and *function* we suggest that any time we care to look, we might expect to experience the knee or spinal cord, but not the knee jerk, which is evident only some of the time. This distinction is yet not adequate since the spinal cord is evident only after proper manipulation — surgical exposure — and hence is less distinct as an experience than is the knee jerk, which is evident usually after much less bother — a slight tap. Still we do not expect to eliminate the spinal cord by instructions to a patient, but we can tell him to suppress the knee jerk. Thus the spinal cord becomes *structurally* distinct but less dominant a condition for the knee jerk. We do not expect verbal instructions to patients to alter the *structure* of a patient's nervous system, yet they can have as profound an effect upon their *functions* as surgical incision. This could go on and on, but the terms *function* and *form* or *structure* are scattered randomly above, to the general confusion of what is otherwise unexceptional. I suggest that we drop them. The correlations between observations are reliable, when we have sufficient observations to correlate.

A syndrome in which there are no known observations definitely bearing on damage to the nervous system is not necessarily a neurologic problem of any kind. Evidence of brain damage by conventionally acceptable means would immediately add it to the established neurologic diagnoses and extend, by its characteristics, our awareness of neurologic signs. When verbal instructions and conversion hysteria can alter *behavior* as elemental as knee jerks and sensation, I see no *a priori* reason for ascribing an unknown *behavioral* syndrome to *brain damage.*

Bill of Particulars

There remains one more consideration, the features of the syndrome called "minimal brain damage" and their correlations including the statistics. As I began, "brain damage" is primarily evident on inspection of nervous tissue by appropriate means; indirectly, it is an accepted diagnosis when supported by established neurologic signs. There are many people whose brain damage has been established by one or both means. Those who have experienced penetrating wounds of the head and brain surgery, the cerebral-palsied, and those who have suffered stroke come to mind. How do they act? Without going into details, it is sufficient to say they act in varied ways. Some are severely handicapped, some appear normal, some present oddities of thinking and behavior, and others get along without notice in the community in roles of some competence. The *fact* of brain damage, established as above, is correlated with no one picture, as we might have expected from the foregoing. "Brain damage" is too broad a category. If we are going to establish a syndrome, we shall have to designate it by the features which brought it to attention, and then see whether we can correlate these in any meaningful manner with other experience, including the possibility of independently detected brain damage.

Again, some definitions might be useful. *Syndrome* means *running together;* and it refers to the combination of traits which, *running together,* serve as sorting criteria for putting people into pigeon holes. It is different from *disease* in that *disease,* in addition, requires an established underlying cause and implies something deranged, whereas a syndrome could be a variant of normal. *Normal* might be called *that which we accept without concern,* a definition which allows openly that one man's normal might not be another's, either within himself or in what he observes. *Normal* bears definition here because it stands usually in opposition to *disease* and *abnormal,* which we enquire into anxiously. To become enquiring of a syndrome that we have noted verges on making a disease of it even before we know anything important about it. Patient rather than anxious enquiry might constrain us to leave some questions and concerns unanswered till we know how to answer them suitably.

There are children who fidget, flit about, get into things, seem unable to ignore the trivial or attend long to the important, have tantrums on slight frustration, yet stare vacantly into space at times. In school and among peers they do poorly, and they lag socially and academically. They tend to think concretely and may have trouble with reading or arithmetic. In their flitting encounters with their environment, they are impossible to predict, and being responsible for them means constant vigilance if they are to be protected and their surroundings preserved from chaos. Their parents are worn out. In short, this is a caricature of childhood. To exhausted adults who must care for these children, it is a problem they wish to understand and to relieve, with or without understanding. There are natural questions like "Why is he like that?", "What can we do?" and "What's to become of him?"

Admittedly, the description is a stereotype; no actual child need fit the pattern above exactly. Each child would be expected to have traits individually his own, and other writers have itemized the disturbing behavior differently. Nevertheless, a stereotype under names like "the hyperkinetic, brain-damaged child" or "the minimally brain-damaged child" has emerged in the past two and a half decades, more or less bracketted by the reports of Werner and Strauss[1] and of Pasamanick and Knobloch.[2]

As a syndrome, a grouping of traits, this stereotype is descriptively clear, and children can be found who fit it well enough. Who are they? Some have had meningitis or encephalitis, some were produced by abnormal pregnancy or difficult delivery, some have had seizures, some have experienced head injury, and others have not had such clearly documented trouble but have had undiagnosed illnesses or other possible threats to their brains. There are some children who come from unusual families or who otherwise stir speculation that they might be seriously emotionally disturbed. Many present no convenient attraction to a physician's attention except their behavior. They tend to come for evaluation between three and seven years of age, as parents wear out and schools can't accept them. Some may have been placid babies; some were not. By adolescence, some are delinquent, and some are functioning effectively. In any event, the specifics of the stereotype are evident mainly after infancy and before puberty. I shall leave remaining aspects of these problems to others and focus, as a neurologist, on the use of "brain-damaged" in the label.

Moot Decision

"Brain-damaged" in the term "minimally brain-damaged child" unobtrusively bears several meanings. Some of these children *are* brain-damaged by known agent or in manifestation of some neurologic signs, and others well *may be*. By vague implication, it might also be taken to mean that the behavior noted is a consequence of the brain damage. Almost as a conclusion, then, "brain damage" blankets the whole group as a diagnosis, and the features of the syndrome become pretenders to the state of neurologic sign. For purpose of immediate discussion, I shall pare the group to those who present no usual neurologic evidence by history or examination, for I am not disputing possibility of brain damage in any child but am interested in the status of the syndrome as evidence of damage to the nervous system. By this approach, there is little to add to what already I have said more generally. Until demonstrable damage to specific parts of the brain is correlated with this clinical picture, the question remains open.

This conclusion is by no means intended to cut off speculation. Several possible sites of damage can be reasonably suggested, by slight extension of some laboratory and clinical experience. For instance, the behavior displayed might be interpreted as resulting from the short attention span, and known structures bearing on the alerting phenomenon come to mind as places to look for signs of damage. Amphetamine, a stimulant, occasionally calms these children. Such paradoxical responses could result from "waking up" the attention span a bit. Nevertheless, speculation is proof of no kind, and we shall probably have to wait a long time for evidence. Meanwhile speculation should not be restricted to neurology alone. Psychiatrists can be busy speculating and observing as well. Nor should speculation be restricted to the "abnormal," for conceivably we could be watching an aberrant development in which the *attention span* waits until adolescence to mature. Secondary problems of management are considerable, and psychologic consequences are not to be ignored, but perhaps nothing went "wrong" at all. Probably, as with syndromes frequently, a varied group has been gathered together and many or all hypotheses may be correct, each for some.

Guilt by Association

It seems to have been the history or implication of brain damage in some of these children which stirred concern about the syndrome as a "brain-damaged" one. If all patients had had acceptably established brain damage, the usual attitude of neurologists, I am sure, would be expectant waiting for evidence bearing on the *structures* involved. If there had been no implication of conventional neurologic evidence in any of these children, "brain-damage" as a label likely would have occurred only to those who despair of understanding unusual behavior otherwise. Clearly, the approach was a statistical one. As a means of summarizing complex and extensive information or of comparing the not quite comparable, statistics are invaluable. If statistics were applied to show, say, that more children with the syndrome had a suggestion of brain damage than is general in the population, and if correlation of the syndrome with brain damage had a significant measureable probability, no one would argue. Note however, that *correlation* is not *cause,* and if we use a probability as an established concept, we are well on the way toward obscuring whatever other correlations there may be and toward diagnosing brain damage by definition rather than by evidence. Calling this syndrome "brain-damaged" with or without qualification urges us to make this error.

If we overlook these reservations, a properly grounded neurologist can seem particularly stubborn and can prompt one to wonder what a neurologist is for when he objects to applying "brain-damaged" to the children described by Werner and Strauss, and Pasamanick and Knobloch, and yet he agrees that some of these children have brain damage. In this instance, his function is clear. He is a member of the jury who demands his reasonable doubts be dispelled before he concurs in a verdict of "Guilty, as charged!"

REFERENCES

1. Werner, H., and Strauss, A.: *J Abnorm Soc Psychol, 36*:236-48, 1941.
2. Pasamanick, B., and Knobloch, H.: *JAMA, 170*:1384-87, 1959.

PART TWO
EDUCATIONAL STRATEGIES

VI

THE EDUCATIONAL METHODS OF STRAUSS AND LEHTINEN

MORTON BORTNER

T HE IDEAS EXPRESSED BY Strauss and Lehtinen have played an important role in the development of thinking and research in the area of brain injury. Their educational views have gained wide currency. Therefore, it was believed that a concise summary of their views on education of brain-injured children would be of value to the reader. The following summary presents their views[3,4] in the context of their conception of the brain-injured child as a psychological and educational entity.

Cerebral injury, regardless of location and extent, is characterized by a specific set of behaviors. These behaviors are seen with sufficient frequency to warrant their recognition as a syndrome. Special classroom procedures are suggested for the amelioration of these behavioral characteristics on the assumption that undamaged portions of the brain will compensate the disabilities. These behavioral characteristics may be subsumed under three major categories: (1) general behavior disorders, (2) perceptual disturbances, and (3) thinking disorders.

BEHAVIOR DISORDERS

The symptoms of disorder in brain-injured children include clumsiness, awkwardness, and incoordinated and erratic behavior. Hyperactivity and disinhibition are frequently reported and are seen as overflows of motor behavior without clear goals. The brain-damaged child is overactive, directionless, unfocused and pointlessly on the move; in a classroom situation this can be particularly disruptive. Catastrophic reactions are reported, and these consist essentially of the child's responding with great frustration and anxiety to a situation that is in some way overwhelming for him. Intense crying may be one manifestation of this reaction, flight is another.

Inappropriately repetitive or perseverative behavior may appear in the emotional realm in the forms of foolish laughter which goes on and on, automatized activities where a motor act is repeated over and over, and stereotypy of verbal behavior such as incessant and pointless questioning. Some manifestations of the above-mentioned behaviors are developmentally appropriate to certain life stages, and it is therefore essential to be familiar with developmental landmarks and normal behavior in order to know when special significance should be attributed to the behavior of a given child. Any one of these behaviors in extreme form, and certainly several acting together, will constitute a serious hindrance to the educational process. These behaviors are obtrusive and therefore must be directly considered in the pedagogical plan for the child.

PERCEPTUAL DISTURBANCES

Perception is seen as a process which develops from primitive and simple in young organisms to more inclusive and complex in more mature organisms, but always with the characteristics of the whole and its related parts. As the child grows older he sees more details, integrates them more successfully into the whole, and indeed sees larger and more complex wholes. It is within this Gestalt orientation that Strauss and Lehtinen describe various perceptual difficulties associated with brain injury.

Perceptual disturbances are described in terms of part-whole relationships or figure-ground relationships. The background stimulus distracts the child's attention from the figure. On the marble board test, for example, which requires the child to construct designs by placing marbles into recesses, brain-injured children show characteristic modes of handling the task which reflect a lower order or more confused method of attack. They are *forced* to respond to certain background features of the stimulus which are task-irrelevant and which interfere with adequate performance. Similar difficulties may be seen in a variety of visual, tactual, and auditory task situations, and this implies the action of a general organismic difficulty rather than one which is task-specific.

Another aspect of perceptual impairment, discussed in terms of Goldstein's concept of *forced responsiveness,* is that of perseveration. This consists of repetitious activity which is inappropriate to the task-demands. Examples consist of saying the same numbers over and over when asked to count, or of writing with interminable repetition a newly learned letter or word. The distinction is made between repetitive perserveration, with a given response repeated consecutively, and iterative perseveration, with a certain response made intermittently like an unwanted and recurring theme.

THINKING DISORDERS

On the basis of the kinds of sorting tasks so frequently used in studies dealing with concept formation, (see, for example, Halstead, 1940) [1] brain-injured children are described as given to "uncommon, far fetched and often peculiar" responses. In one variation of the sorting task, the child is shown and asked to identify a variety of objects. He is then asked to "sort" or to group those objects which "go together." Brain-injured children according to Strauss and Werner (1942) [2] tend to sort in a manner which distinguishes them from mental age-related normal peers and retarded children without neurological impairment. They sort according to form and color, unessential details, or according to vague or imaginary relationships instead of sorting on the basis of common class membership or functional relatedness of objects. In a less-structured task where the imaginative capacities of the child were studied, Strauss and Werner reported brain-injured children as pedantic and meticulous, making more uncommon choices and being somewhat "loose" in the connections and arrangements they formed among objects. They stressed the parallels to be found in the thinking behavior of brain-injured children and brain-injured adults. With this general description of brain-injured children as a background, the authors offer a variety of suggestions as to how to educate them. These suggestions are subsumed under the following formats: (1) general principles, (2) perceptual problems, (3) reading, (4) arithmetic, and (5) writing.

General Principles

The brain-damaged organism is unselectively over-responsive to a parade of environmental stimuli, many of which are irrelevant to the task at hand. This difficulty manifests itself as psycho-motor distractibility with the child flitting physically from one place, person, or object to another without conscious motive. Another manifestation of the same disorder consists of loose associations or the intrusion of unrelated ideas which pull the child's attention in all directions even while he is sitting quietly, thus preventing him from concentrating in a meaningful way on a particular stimulus and the requirements of an assigned task. Thus, distractibility need not be expressed merely on a psycho-motor level. The child may be so attentive to details that he fails to learn the larger meanings of his assignment. Ironically, because of failure to achieve assigned goals, these children are often considered inattentive. It would be more accurate to consider such children as improperly focused.

The approach to children with this problem is to simplify the task by additional explanation, demonstration, more extensive sequencing, or whatever else helps to focus the child's attention. Children who show especially confused, erratic behavior or breakdowns in effective functioning can be helped through the medium of anticipatory explanation. That is, before the child is required to respond, it is explained to him what he will experience, what he is expected to do, and all else that will eliminate ambiguity and potential anxiety.

In interpersonal relations, hyperactivity, disinhibition and distractibility are manifested in aggressive behavior. Verbal attempts to alter this behavior are ineffectual. Primary disabilities such as distractibility may, in addition to interfering with effective classroom learning, also have an unfortunate effect on the emotional life of the child. His feelings of self-regard may be adversely affected as a consequence of repeated experience of failure. Educational recommendations therefore need to deal with emotional consequences attendant to the primary disorders.

In general, there are two approaches taken to remedy the

educational problems engendered by distractibility, disinhibition, hyperactivity and their emotional consequences. First, the environment of the child is structured, and second, the child is educated to exercise controls from within.

It is recommended that the child's environment be so-structured and simplified as to protect him from distraction. Procedures which require his participation should stress explicitness and orderliness. Routine is also helpful since it enables him to predict events of the day and thereby gain a measure of security.

It is helpful when children can tell where they are going during the course of a learning experience. It is also helpful for them to get a sense of successful completion. To facilitate these goals, the lesson plan should include many short tasks with initial, extremely brief learning tasks, perhaps lasting not more than one or two minutes. Anything which detracts from task orientation is either eliminated or reduced. Therefore, pictures on a page or other pages in a workbook may be eliminated or removed from view if they interfere with task-orientation, and by the same token the very complexity of the expected response may be reduced, if that too is interfering with the child's capacity to attend to the task.

The tendency to respond to details rather than to essentials may reflect an incapacity to delay a response until all the data are considered. The child seizes upon the first recognizable element, however unimportant, and acts as if that is the essential or central element in the task. Therefore, tasks which give practice in delaying the response are helpful to these children. Riddles starting with a generality and resulting in a specific instance (or the reverse) are recommended as useful means of helping the child learn to revise repeatedly the meaning attributed to the initial generality; thus he learns to delay a final conclusion. Since the teacher is part of the child's environment, it is recommended that she minimize the ornamentation of her dress; bracelets, earrings, pins and necklaces may be distracting to the child. Visual stimulation deriving from outside the classroom can be reduced by covering the lower portion of the windows. It is also recommended that irrelevant auditory stimuli be reduced, and that street sounds and the sounds of other classrooms be eliminated by the strategic placement of the classroom.

Structuring the classroom implies, in addition to the elimination of distracting visual and auditory stimuli, the tactical arrangement of children. Children should be seated at sufficient distance from one other to guarantee a minimum of unnecessary contact. Since these changes cannot be effectively carried out in regular classes, special classes are encouraged. Small groups not exceeding twelve in number are recommended. Even with the minimized interaction implied by small groups, large rooms, and ample space between children's seats, there are occasions when it is necessary to further delimit interaction and its consequent stimulation. This is accomplished by placing the distractible child at one or another point in a continuum of relative isolation from the group. He may be removed to the outer periphery of the class, he may be placed facing a wall, or he may be placed behind a screen. In all cases, of course, the purpose of the move is carefully explained to the child.

To counteract the tendency to respond to irrelevant details, it is recommended that such details be simply eliminated whenever possible. Certain picture illustrations and borders in books may be considered extraneous. Such extraneous stimuli may be eliminated through the use of such devices as cover pages with cut out slots which permit selected areas of a page to be seen. The interest that distractible children show for moving stimuli suggests a useful intervention; that is, classroom procedures should include a variety of opportunities for controlled motor expressions.

The second goal of the teacher, to encourage controls from within, is achieved through the gradual transition toward more general classroom practice. The emphasis on structure is lessened in the expectation that the child will, through reduced disturbance and increased competence, become able to provide the necessary internal controls.

Perceptual Problems

Perceptual problems are especially evident when the child is expected to respond to two-dimensional copy as contrasted with

three-dimensional objects. There is a need to develop special instructional procedures to counteract this difficulty. Recommended
procedures include building block structures to match flat copy,
placing pegs according to a given pattern, and sorting designs according to shape. This last procedure is enhanced by intensifying
the figure-ground aspect of the design, namely coloring in the
figure or outlining its contour with a broad stroke. Perceiving contour is seen as a step in the direction of being able to equate flat
copy with three-dimensional objects. Such perceptual generalization is seen as imperceptible transitioning to higher level generalizations made according to function or use. This transition is
helped by assigning tasks such as sorting pictures or words, first
according to one principle and then according to another.

The child's capacity to maintain interest in complex tasks will
be enhanced as a function of improved perceptual adequacy. Instead of showing rapid satiation and requiring a rapid succession
of new stimuli, the child whose perceptions are improved shows
interest in new combinations of stimuli of which he was previously
unaware, and indeed, shows the capacity to look at more complex
aspects of stimuli.

Repetition is not considered generally helpful in the process
of enhancing perceptual adequacy. If an initial perception were
in error, additional repetition experience with the same stimulus
might lead to perpetuation of the same error. In normal children,
awareness of error occurs spontaneously, whereas brain-injured
children require special training. For example, it may be necessary to counteract the defective visual discrimination feedback
which fails to inform the child when he is not accurately writing
a newly learned letter. Repetition may be more helpful when it is
possible to introduce slight variations in task-demands. For example, arithmetic examples can be solved horizontally as well as
vertically, and words can be substituted for numbers. By thus
altering minor aspects of a task without changing its essential
point, it becomes possible to recognize basic similarities in the
context of superficial differences, and the generalizibility of the
task-demand itself is more clearly understood.

The ability to anticipate and to predict is seen as grounded in perceptual experience. The child should be able to predict, for example, whether or not a certain group of beads will be sufficient for a given addition problem. Thereby he can gain the perceptual experience which acts as the necessary background for more complex predictions.

Unstable figure-ground relations and poor form perception constitute important problem areas. It is suggested that patterns and contours will be effectively organized and delineated by the use of heavy outlining and color cues. Such organizing and delineating is seen as contributing to greater stability of figure and ground. Commercial materials such as workbooks are often too complex or too productive of distraction. It is suggested that they are better used as occasional sources of work where the discretion of the teacher can be exercised. Distracting, unimportant, and confusing details can be eliminated, separate pages can be cut out, and the rate at which specific tasks are given may be geared to the needs of the child.

Materials are favored which can be constructed both by the teacher and the child. When children participate in the construction of materials, their comprehension of the expected task is sometimes thereby enhanced. It is important that the materials be such as to permit the child to use them relatively independently, thus freeing him from dependence on the teacher and those negative feelings of self which may be consequent to such dependency. Apparently, once a given process is understood and the child feels secure in his acquired competence, earlier needed special devices, materials, and aids are spontaneously discarded.

The use of special activities such as playing "store," rather than being used as a method directed to new learning, is recommended as a means of determining whether an already acquired skill has been fully established. The multidimensional and highly distracting character of such special activities provides the opportunity to test the ability of the child to add, even in the excitement of a game. However, the very nature of the child's deficits, namely, forced responsiveness to irrelevant stimuli, suggests that such a complex situation is not one in which the initial learning should take place.

Automatic responses are verbal formulas learned without comprehension; they are frequent among the brain-injured because of good facility in verbal memory in such children. Such automatizations are, of course, misleading because they lead the teacher to overestimate the child's comprehension. Such verbal formulas are often achieved through drill. It is recommended that procedures which emphasize insights and understanding be favored over repetitions and drills. Perseverative responses are most likely to occur in the face of difficulty. A difficult word may be repeatedly misread, misspelled, or incorrectly sounded or written. Directing the child to another activity with eventual return to the source of difficulty has been found helpful.

Overly meticulous work habits are in some children a hindrance rather than a help. Many children with strong needs for orderliness will spend as much time spelling out neat letters or numbers as in arriving at answers to questions. With such children it is helpful to emphasize oral work, assign short tasks, and set time limits. Other children are quite variable in their performance and productivity. A competence achieved on one day may be followed by failure at a later time. Since such unevenness is in part attributed to the child's fluctuating responsiveness and hypersensitivity to extraneous aspects of his environment, it is suggested that new learning be deferred on such occasions and demands be kept to a minimum. When the child has been brought to a functioning level of high third or fourth grade, he may be expected to make progress in the regular class without special instruction.

Arithmetic

Gestalt psychology is offered as the theoretical orientation within which specific instructional procedures for the teaching of arithmetic are developed. It is assumed that number concept is based on the perceptual organization of visual-spatial stimuli and on the relating of parts and whole in such a scheme. Teaching arithmetic, within this context, consists of developing an adequate visual-spatial scheme based on organized perceptual experiences which, in turn, form the basis for abstract number concepts. The visual-spatial system is abstracted from the concrete perceptual experiences of the child, and thus serves as a basis for later development of the more abstract system of number concept. Since brain-injured children have disturbances in basic perceptual organizing ability, they require special instructional procedures and materials to help them in arithmetic.

Some children depend on intact verbal facility and learn arithmetic problems by rote memory, but without the necessary underlying perceptual scheme they will remain unable to attach much meaning to these problems. Hence, it is perceptual adequacy that needs to be enhanced as a prelude to learning arithmetic.

Early instruction consists of sorting and matching of small groups. The matching of identical groups may be facilitated by using different colors for different size groups. Sequential counting is taught next. Since many distractible children lose their place and skip or repeat, aids may be profitably used to insure correct sequencing. Devices found helpful in counting include moveable slides which permit the gradual exposure of an increasing number of dots, and the use of different color cues for different size groups. A more complex and later step is the recognition and naming of the parts of the group. Simple counting of the separate elements of a visually presented group of objects requires coordination between verbal, visual, and motor behavior. The general disorders of distractibility and hyperactivity may actively interfere with the proper integration of such a complex activity. Naming a unit may run ahead of touching it. Therefore, devices are recommended which will facilitate the correspondence of visualizing, touching, and naming. Placing wooden sticks in boxes with corresponding holes and fitting blocks on pegs are examples of devices in which the very complexity of the motor activity forces the child to slow down and to coordinate more effectively the verbal, visual, and motor responses.

An advanced aspect of counting consists of the ability to form groups. A child asked to form a group of five blocks may not stop at five, but may in a disinhibited manner go on to form a larger group despite adequate comprehension. Recommended techniques for counteracting this problem include presenting the child with a card that has the required number of dots; the child's task is to

cover each dot with a block. A later step requires the child to reproduce similar configurations using the blocks without the dots.
Multiple-choice procedures are also helpful. When the child is
not able to actively form a group of, say, five objects, he can usually experience more success in the less difficult task of selecting
from among an array of choices.

Combining of numbers, as in addition of *three* and *five,* is
preceded by combining groups of objects, as in the addition of
three blocks and five blocks. When small groups can be successfully combined, the learning of number symbols begins. Visual-
perceptual difficulties with the form of the number symbol are
counteracted through the use of kinesthetic and color cues. The
use of number symbols is, of course, initially used in conjunction
with concrete counterparts. More complete knowledge of a number groups is achieved through learning the relative distances between numbers, and the breakdowns of given larger numbers into
their components. The use of concrete configurations such as
three-dot triangles and four-dot squares are also helpful. Such
configurations may be used in association with the number symbol to reinforce the quantitative meaning underlying the symbol.
They are analyzed into subsegments so that *three* is seen as including *one* and *two* and is also seen to be obtained when *two* is removed from *five.* Progress in such analyses is inferred when the
child moves from easier three-dimensional configurations using
blocks or beads, through two-dimensional configurations using
dot drawings, through number symbols alone.

The abacus is an important aid in early learning. Initially, the
abacus may contain color cues with beads on different rows having
different colors; later, all the beads may be the same color. The
combining and taking away of groups lead to an understanding
of addition and substraction. Peseverative children sometimes
find the taking away process interfered with by the opposite movements of the previously learned adding or combining of groups.
Such children require the help of additional devices. These include a card with printed dots in sequence which slides from
view into a cover, slide rule fashion, where dots may be taken
away one by one. Another device, called the "take away box," is

a replica of the abacus in fixed form inside a wooden box with a transparent cover. A metal strip slides across the top of the cover. It can "take away" from a given row by the simple expedient of separating the beads into those on the left and those on the right of the strip. Those difficulties encountered by perseverative children on the abacus are not encountered here since the beads are not actually moved in either direction and are therefore not a source of conflicting tendencies. Relational concepts are deficient in these children and thus require special attention. There is need to stress, wherever feasible, such concepts as *bigger, smaller, louder, softer, darker,* and *lighter.* It may be better, sometimes, to avoid situations where these concepts are necessarily obscure.

Higher level operations are taught according to those principles elaborated for the simpler operations. Concrete materials should be used when necessary. Stress is put on understanding the process rather than relying on memory and automatic solutions. When necessary, special materials should be devised by the teacher to overcome the identified handicap. Those materials described earlier are illustrative of the kinds of aids that are helpful.

Reading

Reading disability in brain-injured children is viewed as another manifestation of the more general disturbances of behavior and perception. Remedial training is therefore addressed to these disturbances rather than showing any special concern for emotional conflicts, interests, or motivation. The latter are viewed as exacerbating rather than causative factors.

Those difficulties in visual perception which contribute to reading disability include: inability to distinguish similar letters; difficulty with word configurations that are similar because of form, or because they contain the same letters in different order, or because of similar prominent details; and inability to spatially sequence letters. When such difficulties are seen in reading, other more general visual-perceptual disturbances are usually found.

Clinical observations suggest that defective auditory perception is also implicated in reading disability. Difficulties are observed in differentiation of speech sounds, in establishing a phonic approach to new words, in appreciating auditory sequence or spatial organization of sounds, and in blending or synthesizing isolated sound units.

Opportunities for the expression of general disturbances such as disinhibition, distractibility, perseveration and hyperactivity are always present and must therefore be considered in the planning of a given remedial procedure and in the structuring of the classroom environment itself. Since language development as a factor in reading readiness is not characteristically defective in brain-injured children, and since excellent resource material already exists for those children who do have difficulty in this area, emphasis is placed on perceptual activities. These include discrimination, spatial organization, figure-ground and part-whole relations. All of these abilities are involved in putting together jigsaw puzzle pieces. Puzzles are made by cutting pictures from magazines. Their complexity both in terms of content and number of pieces is easily controlled. Discrimination ability is utilized in matching geometric designs. Color cues are helpful in correcting errors on the more complex geometric designs. Quick exposure to designs with subsequent matching gives practice in the skill of perceiving a total visual entity as contrasted with part-details.

Exercises related directly to reading include those which deal with the perception of letters. Learning to discriminate the letter forms is facilitated by making sets of alphabet cards, sorting identical letters, and using color cues to overcome directional confusions. To further solidify recognition, letters may be cut into jigsaw puzzle parts to be reconstructed later.

Matching a word is a readiness experience. The selection of the match is initially made from among "distractor" words that are quite different from the key word; the task is made progressively more difficult when the distractor words are made increasingly similar to the key word. It is not necessary for the child to know what the word means or how it is pronounced. Emphasis is simply on recognition.

Since distractibility may interfere with the process of reading sentences in a continuous manner and result in diverse, irrelevant behavior, aids which counter this tendency of the child to leave the field are encouraged. Cutting out separate sentences for pasting, and separating contiguous words from each other within a sentence by using bits of color are recommended. Use of markers and fingers for pointing is also helpful in preventing the child from rushing blindly ahead, and in emphasizing the foreground character of the word against the background of the page and other words.

Instruction in auditory perception is recommended as a means of helping the brain-injured child acquire a basic sight vocabulary. Many of these children do not spontaneously recognize the generalization that printed symbols may be equated with speech sounds. They benefit from further analyses of sounds and their relations to visual counterparts. Early auditory analysis includes focus on sound itself without visual counterparts. Oral emphasis permits gradual recognition of isolated sound units occurring in words. This is supplemented with the activity of searching for pictures which contain given sounds. Sound blending is helped through the use of multiple-choice techniques. Pictures illustrating several blends are shown to the child. The teacher offers a multiple-choice of blend sounds from which the child matches to the appropriate picture. The emphasis here is on the recognition of the blend rather than its production. After the auditory discrimination is made, the visual symbol may be presented.

All of the exercises discussed in connection with both visual and auditory discrimination are illustrative of what may be termed an analytical approach as contrasted with a global approach. The former stresses part-whole relations; the latter stresses recognition and memory of totalities.

The stress on accurate visual and auditory perception is viewed as merely the necessary prelude to the eventual integration of these two modes of receiving information. The procedures discussed emphasize only the acquisition of reading skills since this is such a frequent area of deficit. More complex problems such as difficulties in comprehension are seen as reflecting damage to that area of the brain concerned with the thinking process. Or, the child may have skills, but he may be unable to relate the statements he reads to an external perceptual word. Reading ability, at this level, is helped indirectly through the enhancement of conceptual and perceptual adequacies.

Writing

The goals of teaching writing are aimed less at communication, per se, and more at developing the perceptual processes of visual-motor integration. Indirectly, through the use of kinesthetic cues, writing should enhance the learning of reading. Writing readiness is enhanced by procedures such as tracing and copying of lines and designs drawn in a variety of orientations and by use of modeling clay and stylus in place of pencil and paper as a means of emphasizing kinesthetic cues.

Cursive writing is recommended as it obviates the problem of spacing letters properly, contributes to the perception of total word units, and encourages the concept that order and sound rather than symbol form are significant in the reading process. Letters are taught in relation to ease of motor movements involved, that is, those letters easiest made are taught first. (Any material contributing to motor facility and to the overcoming of clumsiness is incorporated into the teaching method: for example, large, soft-lead pencils, lined paper, and color cues outlining the space to be written in.) Letters are taught individually at first and combined with the articulation of the sound. This is followed by combining letters, both written and articulated, which in turn is followed by the increased demand to write from memory. The use of pens with colored inks has been found to lend interest to the writing task. In general, the approach recommended is one that views writing as essentially grounded in accurate perceptions rather than in motor skills.

SUMMARY

The educational methods of Strauss and Lehtinen have been summarized. Within the context of their view of the brain-damaged child, suggestions have been outlined which are aimed at remediating basic, underlying inadequacies and consequent difficulties in reading, writing, and arithmetic.

REFERENCES

1. Halstead, W. C.: Preliminary analysis of grouping behavior in patients with cerebral injury by the method of equivalent and non-equivalent stimuli. *Am J Psychiat, 96:*1263-94, 1940.
2. Strauss, A. A., and Werner, H.: Disorders of conceptual thinking in the brain-injured child. *J Nerv Ment Dis, 96:*153-72, 1942.
3. Strauss, A. A., and Lehtinen, Laura: *Psychopathology and Education of the Brain-injured Child.* New York, Grune, 1947.
4. Strauss, A. A., and Kephart, N.: *Psychopathology and Education of the Brain-injured Child. Vol. 2, Progress in Theory and Clinic.* New York, Grune, 1955.

VII

TEACHING THE CHILD WITH A PERCEPTUAL-MOTOR HANDICAP

NEWELL C. KEPHART

ONE OF THE MAJOR SYMPTOMS attributed to the brain-injured child is a perceptual-motor handicap. Although not all children falling within the general category of brain-injured display this symptom, it seems apparent that large numbers of them do. During the last few years a great deal of attention has been given to the perceptual-motor problems of these children. Inevitably, in the early stages of such work, major emphasis was given to the problem of diagnosis and evaluation of the perceptual-motor handicap. In more recent years, however, it has been possible to move beyond the diagnosis and evaluation stage and to give increasing attention to the problems of teaching and training.

It should be emphasized that when we speak of a perceptual-motor handicap we are not concerned entirely with the child who has a specific motor defect resulting from an injury to the motor aspects of the central nervous system. Although this specific defect group does in fact display many of the perceptual-motor difficulties, these same problems exist in children in whom no specific motor involvement can be determined. This latter group of children manifests the effects of injury primarily through more generalized behavior symptoms. The perceptual-motor performance of such children is frequently described as clumsy or awkward. They may be limited in their motor responses, and these responses may be inaccurate. They may attain reasonably high degrees of motor skills in specific activities. However, this motor accomplishment does not generalize to similar activities but remains highly specific to a particular movement or series of movements. These children lack flexibility in all types of motor performance, and they have difficulty in readily adapting motor responses to changes in external environmental conditions.

On the perceptual side, these children have difficulty in establishing an adequate coordination between the hand and the eye. They are frequently able, for example, to identify and name a form but have great difficulty in reproducing it on paper. They are frequently overly impressed with the details of a form, and they respond to these details rather than responding to the total form. They tend to lack a spatial orientation; their responses indicate that they have difficulty maintaining *their* relationships to objects in space, and they cannot perceive relationships *between* objects in space. Perceptual data and motor responses frequently appear to act independently of each other. The close relationship between perceptual activity and motor activity, which is signified by the hyphenated term *perceptual-motor,* is not as firm in these children as it is in normal children. Therefore, behavior tends to be disrupted since perceptual judgment and motor responses are coordinated closely with each other.

The approach to teaching such a child appears to depend in large part on our ability to supply the perceptual-motor skills which the child has found difficult to develop for himself. The child must live in a world where normal perceptual-motor activities are usually taken for granted. Therefore, most of the problems which he faces and the activities in which he is asked to participate are organized and constructed on the assumption of normal perceptual-motor skills. Although it is sometimes possible to modify specific activities so that the required performance avoids the child's handicap, such external modifications are of limited use in a total-life situation which is designed otherwise. It is therefore usually more desirable to try to provide the child with the skills assumed by the world around him. Insofar as these skills can be supplied, the child can respond to the environment around him in a broader and more efficient manner. Although there are certain types of handicaps which will require external modifications of the type described because of one or more specific interferences with the perceptual-motor process, the goal in teaching should be to rely upon such modifications only when necessary. The more constructive goal envisages providing the child with as many of the essential skills as we can, so that his interaction with his environment can be as wide as possible.

PATTERNS OF MOTOR RESPONSE

The approach to such teaching usually follows a course the reverse of that suggested by the title, perceptual-motor. It has been found advantageous in most cases to give attention first to the development of essential motor patterns. In this respect teaching follows the developmental course of the child. The *initial* learnings of the child were motor learnings, and these initial motor responses formed a basic foundation upon which more advanced learning could be built. These initial motor patterns permit the expansion of learning into other areas and other levels.

It is necessary first to differentiate between a *motor pattern* and a *motor skill.* A motor skill is a relatively specific group of movements designed to accomplish a particular purpose. These movements require a coordination of neuromuscular activities which will produce certain prescribed external movements. However, this neuromuscular coordination is limited to the task at hand and does not necessarily demand nor require the use of more extensive neuromuscular functions, nor the integration of the present activity with the overall activity of the child. A motor pattern, on the other hand, is a broad spectrum of movements, any one or any combination of which may be used to accomplish a specific purpose. The motor pattern is more generalized with more stress placed upon the object of the response and less stress placed upon the method of response.

Walking, for example, may be a *motor skill.* In this event, the child is primarily concerned with the motor activities involved. He must concern himself with the problem of how to put one foot in front of the other. The series of movements resulting in the walk is highly prescribed, and the child has difficulty altering this series of movements when he encounters an obstacle or when outside circumstances demand a change in the motor response.

Locomotion, on the other hand, is a *motor pattern.* The primary attention is given to the purpose of the act — how to get to the goal point. The child may use any one or any combination of a large number of specific responses; he may walk, run, hop, skip, or jump. If he encounters an obstacle, he can alter the motor response to change direction and veer around the obstacle or he can make a further alteration and jump over or duck under the obstacle. All of this is accomplished without any particular attention to the motor response itself; the attention continues to be directed towards the goal.

The child who can only walk must be continuously concerned with one or both of two questions: (1) "How do I put one foot in front of the other?" and (2) "How can I find a path to the goal which will require a minimum of alteration of my walking movements?" The child who can locomote, however, needs to pay little or no attention to either of these two questions. His attention is available for the gathering of information about the goal or about the activity related to the goal. With a motor pattern, the child is free to explore and experiment. With a motor skill, he is free only to fulfill certain prescribed activities.

The child with a perceptual-motor handicap has encountered an interference with the processes required for the development of motor patterns. This interference may be neurological, or it may have its origin elsewhere in the developmental process. It has, however, resulted in difficulty with certain types of motor experimentation. As a result of this interference, the child has found it difficult to learn certain types of motor responses and particularly to broaden and elaborate these responses into the more generalized motor patterns. As a result, he frequently possesses a large number of specific motor skills. These specific skills, because of the attention given to them and because of the level of performance developed, may make him appear very competent in motor activities. However, if an alteration is introduced in the motor response, if an obstacle is placed in the path of his walk, or if he is asked to walk over different and unfamiliar surfaces, the walking skill is frequently found to break down easily. He has not been able to generalize a walking skill into a pattern of locomotion. Whenever variation is required of the motor response so that the specific skills developed are no longer adequate, the response breaks down and the motor behavior becomes disorganized, inaccurate, or ceases completely. It is obvious that such behavior would readily suggest descriptive terms such as awkward or clumsy.

The behavior, however, is not indicative of lack of skill as these adjectives would imply, but rather it shows a lack of flexibility in motor response.

This rigidity of motor response plagued the child from the earliest stages of his learning activities. He was not able to explore the space around him because he had to be too concerned with how to move from one place to another. He was not able to determine the nature of objects by manipulation because he was too concerned with retaining hand contact with the object. He could not investigate the movement of objects in the outside environment because he could not bring his body into relationship with the path of the moving object. All kinds of early experimentation through which tactual and kinesthetic information about the environment should have been obtained were difficult or impossible for him. Even more important, the relationship between the perceptual information coming from the environment and the motor information regarding his responses to the environment should have been correlated. As a result of his deficit, the child found himself in increasing difficulty day by day in maintaining a valid relationship with his environment.

Although there are many motor patterns which are desirable for the child, there are four which are particularly important to education due to their significance in relation to the exploration of the environment.

Posture and Maintenance of Balance

This pattern involves a series of activities by which the child's relationship to gravity is maintained, even though the nature of application of the force of gravity may be altered; or parts of the child's body may be in unusual positions in which the general relationships of the parts to the center of gravity are changed. Important here is flexibility in postural adjustment so that the child can maintain his relationship to gravity even though he moves in a large number of different ways in relation to the center of gravity. Also involved are relationships to gravity where variations are required with respect to the base or support of the body. Such activities as balancing on a rail, standing on one foot, and maintaining balance on supports of limited extent (such as a post) are indicative of the child's ability to maintain his relationship to gravity.

The ability to sense a shift in the relationship of the body parts which alters the balance is required, and the ability to compensate quickly and adequately for these changes with appropriate movements is demanded. These compensatory movements should be adequate, but they should not be overcompensatory. They should be made with only the movement of those parts required for compensation rather than demanding a readjustment of the entire body to restore balance. The child's posture and balance should be highly flexible so that he can make all kinds of movements under all sorts of conditions and still maintain his fundamental relation to the force of gravity.

It is through this pattern that the child maintains a point of origin for the explorations which he will make. The relationships in space are relative, as Einstein has pointed out. The euclidean coordinates of space are also relative. They first develop within the child. He learns the relationship, "the object is in such and such a direction from me." This is the stage of *subjective* spatial relationships; only later does the child develop the *objective* relationships of "object *A* is in such and such a direction from object *B*." In both the subjective and objective stage, the point of origin for the coordinates of space is the line of gravity through the body. The zero point for the concepts *right-left, up-down, behind-before* is the point of contact of the body with the force of gravity. Unless this zero point is well-established, the coordinates cannot become reliable or valid. If, on the other hand, the zero point is too rigid, then the necessary explorations to establish the coordinates cannot be made or are made in an inadequate fashion. Therefore, the pattern of posture and maintenance of balance is essential to the very initial interactions of the child with his external environment.

Locomotion

The pattern of locomotion involves those activities which may be required to move the body from one place to another. Such activities as creeping, crawling, running, walking, hopping, skipping and jumping are involved. These individual activities must be sufficiently flexible so that they can be altered as the requirements of the environment demand, without deflecting attention from the purpose of the act. The child must be able to use any one of a number of types of movement; he must be able to shift easily from one movement to another as demanded, and he must be able to alter each movement as the conditions of the environment change. Throughout all of this alteration, attention must not be diverted from the goal.

The locomotor pattern is of extreme importance in the learning of the child since it is through this pattern that he explores the spaces around him. By locomoting to an object, he develops the initial learnings which begin to tell him about direction and distance. By altering the direction of his locomotion, he begins to learn about changes in direction. By moving from one object to another, he begins to learn about the relationship of objects in space to each other. By walking along a wall, he begins to learn about a straight line and a straight surface. By walking around a corner, he begins to learn about the intersection of surfaces and their relation to each other at the point of intersection. With his locomotor pattern he explores the relationships within the space surrounding him. If his ability to explore is limited by inadequate locomotor patterns, his experiments will lack depth or extent.

Contact

This is the pattern which involves manipulation with the hand. The three essentials involved in the pattern of contact are reach, grasp, and release. The child must learn how to move the arm and hand and how to move them in a prescribed direction in relation to an object for the purpose of making contact with it. He must then learn how to grasp and retain contact with the object. Last of all he must learn how to let go of the object and go on to something else. Any one or all of these three aspects of manipulation may be restricted. It is through the pattern of manipulation that the child gains initial information about objects. Through manual manipulation, he begins to develop concepts of shape, contour and figure-ground relationships. Psychologists have pointed out for some time the importance of this type of manual manipulation in the early learning of the child.

Receipt and Propulsion

The combined patterns of receipt and propulsion involve the child's relationship to moving objects. Patterns of receipt involve those activities concerned with interposing the body or a body part in the path of a moving object for the purpose of stopping or deflecting the movement. Such activities as catching, trapping, batting and hitting are involved. The patterns of propulsion involve those activities in which an object is moved away from the body. Such specific activities as throwing, pushing and kicking are involved.

It is through the patterns of receipt and propulsion that the child is able to explore the relationship of moving objects in space. These patterns involve estimates of the path, distance, rate of travel, and mass of the moving object. At the point of contact, a check on previous estimates is possible. It is through such types of experimentation that the child learns the nature and effect of movements of objects in the environment which surrounds him.

These movement patterns are essential to exploration and experimentation with the surrounding environment. It is important that they be relatively extensive and flexible enough for exploration to be purposeful. It is out of this initial exploration that the child lays the foundation for concrete environmental relationships which he will later use for interpretation of information given to him perceptually or conceptually. Frequently, the child with a perceptual-motor handicap comes to us without adequate patterns of exploration. If we are to teach him what he needs to know about his environment, we will have to give him an adequate exploratory basis on which to build. Therefore, teaching frequently needs to begin with the development of adequate motor patterns.

TEACHING BALANCE AND POSTURE

Balance can best be taught by activities involving the maintenance of balance on a narrow surface. For this purpose, the walking board is used. The walking board is a piece of two-by-four — ten feet long. This board is raised from the floor by the use of brackets so that it is suspended about two inches above floor level. The brackets are arranged so that the board can be placed with either the four-inch side up or the two-inch side up. A description of the walking board as well as a discussion of preliminary activities for children more severely involved will be found in Kephart.[3] The child should learn to maintain balance while he walks slowly across the board in the forward direction, the backward direction, and the sidewise direction. In the sidewise direction he should be able to move both from right to left (involving a left-foot lead) and from left to right (involving a right-foot lead).

The function to be taught by this activity is general balance and the maintenance of the relationship to gravity. The pertinent learning, therefore, comes when balance is lost and has to be regained. For this reason, the situation should be adjusted so that the child is required to cope with the problem of balance. For the more-handicapped child, it may be necessary to provide help by holding his hand as he walks on the board. In this case he should be encouraged to dispense with this help as soon as possible, and the help should be supplied in such a manner that he is required to attempt to balance by himself at each trial on the board. As he progresses (or in the case of the less-handicapped child) such help will not be required. It is essential to introduce variations in the task as soon as possible. These variations are designed to alter the balance problem so that the child is forced to experiment with the relationship to gravity itself rather than to practice a specific skill of walking on a board.

Such variations will first take the form of increasing the difficulty of the balance task. Thus the board may be placed on the two-inch side instead of on the four-inch side. In addition, however, to increases in the difficulty in a specific task, it will be necessary to introduce other variations which, although they do not alter the level of difficulty, alter the conditions and procedures under which the task must be accomplished. Thus the child may be asked to walk across the board carrying a weight in one hand. The addition of this weight alters the weight relationship of the two sides of the body and requires an alteration in the kind and direction of compensatory movements required. We may also require him to carry a pole which he grasps with both hands. In this case movements on one side of the body are, at least in part, transferred to the other side of the body, thus altering the balancing effect of compensatory movements.

The following list of possible variations in the walking board task has been developed by the department of public instruction of the state of Illinois.*

Balance Beam Exercises

1. Walk forward on beam, arms held sideward.
2. Walk backward on beam, arms held sideward.
3. With arms held sideward, walk to middle, turn around and walk backward.
4. Walk forward to middle of beam, then turn and walk remaining distance sideward-left with weight on balls of feet.
5. Walk to center of beam, then turn and continue sideward-right.
6. Walk forward with left foot always in front of right.
7. Walk forward with right foot always in front of left.
8. Walk backward with left foot always in front of right.
9. Walk backward with right foot always in front of left.
10. Walk forward with hands on hips.
11. Walk backward with hands on hips.
12. Walk forward and pick up a blackboard eraser from middle of beam.
13. Walk forward to center, kneel on one knee, rise and continue to end of beam.
14. Walk forward with eraser balanced on top of head.
15. Walk backward with eraser balanced on top of head.
16. Place eraser at center of beam. Walk to center, place eraser on top of head, continue to end of beam.
17. Have partners hold a wand twelve inches above center of beam. Walk forward on beam and step over wand.
18. Walk backward and step over wand.
19. Hold wand at height of three feet. Walk forward and pass under bar.
20. Walk backward and pass under bar.
21. Walk the beam backward with hands clasped behind body.

*Published by permission of Health and Physical Education Department, Office of the Superintendent of Public Instruction. Ray Page, Superintendent, Springfield, Illinois.

22. Walk the beam forward, arms held sideward, palm down, with an eraser on back of each hand.
23. Walk the beam forward, arms held sideward, palms up, with an eraser on palm of each hand.
24. Walk the beam backward, arms held sideward, palms up, with an eraser on back of each hand.
25. Walk the beam backward, arms held sideward, palms up, with an eraser on palm of each hand.
26. Walk the beam sideward-right, weight on balls of feet.
27. Walk the beam sideward-left, weight on balls of feet.
28. Walk forward to middle of beam, kneel on one knee, straighten right leg forward until heel is on the beam and knee is straight. Rise and walk to end of beam.
29. Walk forward to middle of beam, kneel on one knee, straighten left leg forward until heel is on beam and knee is straight. Rise and walk to end of the beam.
30. Walk backward to middle of beam. Kneel on one knee, straighten right leg forward until heel is on beam and knee is straight. Rise and walk to end of beam.
31. Walk backward to middle of beam, kneel on one knee, straighten left leg forward until heel is on beam and knee is straight. Rise and walk to end of beam.
32. Hop on right foot, the full length of beam.
33. Hop on left foot, the full length of beam.
34. Hop on right foot, the full length of beam, then turn around and hop back.
35. Hop on left foot, the full length of beam, then turn around and hop back.
36. Walk to middle of beam, balance on one foot, turn around on this foot and walk backwards to end of beam.
37. Walk to middle of beam sideward-left, turn around and walk to end sideward-right.
38. With arms clasped about body in rear, walk the beam forward.
39. With arms clasped about body in rear, walk forward to the middle, turn around once, walk backward the remaining distance.
40. Place eraser at middle of beam, walk out on it, kneel on one knee, place eraser on top of head, rise, turn around and walk backward the remaining distance.
41. Walk the beam backward with an eraser balanced on back of each hand.
42. Walk to middle of beam, do a right-side support, rise and then walk to end.
43. Walk to middle of beam, do a left-side support, rise and walk to end.
44. Place eraser on middle of beam. Walk out to it, kneel on one knee,

pick up eraser and place it on beam behind pupil, rise and continue to end.

45. Walk to middle of beam, do a balance stand on one foot, arms held sideward with trunk and free leg held horizontally.

46. Place eraser at middle of beam, walk beam sideward-left, pick up eraser, place it on right side of beam, turn around and walk sideward-right to end of beam.

47. Hold wand fifteen inches above beam. Balance eraser on head, walk forward stepping over wand.

48. Hold wand fifteen inches above beam. Balance eraser on head, walk backward stepping over wand.

49. Hold wand fifteen inches above beam. Balance eraser on head, walk sideward-right, stepping over wand.

50. Hold wand fifteen inches above beam. Balance eraser on head, walk sideward-left, stepping over wand.

51. Hold wand three feet high. Walk forward, hands on hips, and pass under bar.

52. Hold wand three feet high. Walk backward, hands on hips and pass under bar.

53. Hold a piece of paper at right angle so it will stand on beam at the middle. Walk to paper, kneel, pick it up with teeth, rise and walk to end of beam.

54. Place paper as in 53, walk out to it, do a left-side support, pick up paper with teeth and walk to end of beam.

55. Place paper as in 53, walk out to it, do a right-side support, pick up paper with teeth and walk to end of beam.

56. Hop to middle of beam on left foot. Turn around on same foot and hop backward to end of beam.

57. Hop to middle of beam on right foot. Turn around on same foot and hop backwards to end of beam.

58. Walk beam forward, eyes closed.

59. Walk beam sideward, eyes closed.

60. Walk beam backward, eyes closed.

61. Stand on beam, feet side by side, eyes closed, and record number of seconds balance is maintained.

62. Stand on beam, one foot in advance of the other, eyes closed, and record number of seonds balance is maintained.

63. Stand on right foot, eyes closed, and record number of seconds balance is maintained.

64. Stand on left foot, eyes closed, and record number of seconds balance is maintained.

65. Walk beam sideward-left, eyes closed.

66. Partners start at opposite ends, walk to middle, pass each other and continue to end of beam.

67. Place hands on beam, have partner hold legs (as in wheelbarrow race) and walk to end of beam.
68. Same as 67, but partner walks with his feet on beam, instead of the ground, straddling the beam.
69. "Cat walk" on beam, walk on "all fours," hands and feet on beam.

TEACHING CONTACT SKILLS

It is with the skills of hand contact that the child explores the objects with which he comes into contact. Objects presented to him have little significance for learning unless he has sufficient skill to manipulate the objects for the purpose of gaining information. Each of the three aspects of the contact pattern should be considered.

Reach involves the ability to bring the hand into contact with the object. Involved here are not only the muscular skill itself but also the visual appreciation of the location of the object and the ability to bring the hand to a spot which has been visually identified. For the child whose skills in reaching are deficient, activities can be provided offering direct practice in this skill. Thus, objects can be presented to the child, and he can be asked to reach out and touch them. Large objects should be used in the early stages of training in order to provide as large a visual target as possible and to decrease the precision required in the reach. As the child gains skill, the objects can be reduced in size. The pegs used in pegboard activities make good objects for reach. Present the object at various positions with reference to the child's body. They should be presented to the right, to the left, on the midline, above and below the center. At this stage the only requirement of the child is that he reach out and touch the peg.

Although most children have some form of grasp when they enter the school situation, many will be found whose grasp is inadequate. Inadequacy of grasp is evidenced in two ways: Inability to use the thumb opposite the index and middle finger in grasping small objects, and lack of strength in the grasp response.

Looking at the first aspect of grasp, the activities suggested in the discussion of contact can be used. Beginning with larger objects, ask the child to take hold and hang on to the object. As the

object becomes smaller, encourage him to use the thumb-opposi-
tional grip.

To increase the strength of grip, resistance can be added to
these same activities. Thus, the teacher can hold the object after
the child grasps it, requiring him to exert force of grasp to pull
it away. Objects which provide a force opposite to the grasp,
such as spring-type clothespins, can also be used. One very useful
activity is that of attaching spring-type clothespins to the rim of
a can or box. The child is required not only to grasp the clothes-
pin but also to exert pressure of grip in order to open the pin and
hold it open while he places it on the rim. In more gross activities,
hanging from bars and ladders can be used to increase the strength
of grip.

A number of children will show difficulties in the ability to
release an object. These difficulties are usually seen in terms of
timing of the release. Instead of being able to release an object at
a particular instant and in synchrony with an overall activity, the
child releases late, and his release is an unfolding of the hand
rather than a definite movement to release contact with the object.
Activities for training in this area are largely concerned with the
timing of the release function. The child can be asked to drop an
object cleanly at a given time. Thus, the child can be given the
task of dropping objects into a container. In this activity he must
move the hand over the container and "at this point in the act"
release the object. Large objects and relatively large containers
can be used at first, and the size of both the object and the container can be subsequently reduced. As the child's skill increases,
the container can be moved continuously while the child is asked
to pursue the container and drop the object when his hand has
caught up to the moving container.

Auditory information can also be used to aid the child in the
simultaneous release of the two hands. Thus, he can be asked to
put on a table or floor, a block large enough for him to hold with
both hands. If the two hands release simultaneously, the block
falls with only one sound. If the hands are not released simultaneously, there are two sounds — one from the side of the block which

was released first, and a second from the side which was released later.

The child can also be asked to place blocks on the table without dropping them. In this activity he must synchronize his release with the tactual and kinesthetic clues resulting from the contact of the object with the surface. Many of the instances so annoying in the classroom in which these children slam objects about may be because of difficulty in releasing the object at the proper time. Activities designed to teach synchronized release aid frequently in reducing such problems.

The primary purpose of the contact skills is to permit the child to obtain information about objects through motor manipulation. Activities in which he is asked to feel an object and identify it can be used to encourage such manipulation. Identification can either be indicated verbally or by selecting a match from among a group of objects or pictures. One such activity uses a sack filled with a number of objects (spools, pencils, blocks, balls, and toy cars). The child is asked to reach his hand into the bag without looking, select an object, manipulate it with his hand, and tell what it is. He then removes the object from the bag and checks his identification visually.

Similar but more abstract activity presents the child with a form (circle, triangle, or square) cut out of cardboard or thin wood. The form is hidden from the child, and he is asked to explore it with his finger. Upon completion of his exploration, he is asked either to identify from a series of drawings the one which is like what he felt, or he can be asked to draw what he has felt. Such activities encourage the child to use contact skills for the purposes of manipulation and information gathering.

TEACHING SKILLS OF RECEIPT AND PROPULSION

It is through the combined skills of receipt and propulsion that the child investigates movement in the space around him. These skills involve intercepting moving objects or imparting movement to stationary objects. It is through these motor relationships to movement that movement in the external environment becomes meaningful to the child. In both receipt and propulsion the child is required to follow and interpret the movement of an object and to adjust his motor activities to this movement. Training in this area usually starts with the problem of receipt. An object is moved towards the child, and he is required to intercept or alter this movement. The most common activities in this connection are those involving ball play. In the early stages, a ball is rolled slowly toward the child, and he traps it between his legs. The child is seated on the floor with his legs extended, the ball is rolled directly toward him so that interception is easy and only the response of trapping movements is required. The timing of the trapping pattern is not critical since the ball remains in position between the legs until trapped. At a later stage the ball is rolled in the child's general direction, and he is required to alter the position of his legs in order to trap it. At this point, continued visual contact is required, and the trapping pattern must be timed to coincide with the arrival of the ball. The child should be able to contact the moving ball with either leg or with both legs.

When the hands and arms are used instead of the legs, the activity is called catching. It may be found that the thrown ball moves too rapidly for the child to make the necessary adjustments. Therefore, in the early stages of training, it may be necessary for the teacher to hold the ball in her hand and move it slowly toward the child. The child holds his hand and arms in the catching position and contacts the ball when it comes within arm's reach. He should, however, follow the ball visually and predict, upon the basis of this visual information, when it is within arm's reach. Do not permit him to wait until the ball touches his hand and then make the catching movement. In the early stages the ball is moved directly toward the child. As he develops skill, the ball is moved in his direction but not directly toward him, so that he must adjust his arms, hands, or entire body to the direction from which the ball is approaching. The child should be able to contact the moving ball with either hand or with both hands. When both hands are used, they should contact the ball at the same time.

When the child can maintain visual contact and predict the

timing of the catching behavior, the ball is rolled toward him. This activity involves a somewhat more rapid movement of the object and requires him to make the motor adjustments required for catching at a more rapid rate. When he is able to handle the rolled ball, it can be thrown. The thrown ball moves more rapidly, and motor adjustments must be made more precisely and with greater synchrony.

It will be found useful to use other objects to add variation. Particularly, objects which move rather slowly are desirable. In this connection, balloons are very helpful since they move quite slowly and follow an irregular course. A balloon can either be thrown to the child or can be tossed into the air for the child to catch. When he becomes more skillful, he can tap the balloon into the air and tap it again as it falls, thus keeping it in the air. The child can also be asked to contact the moving balloon with parts of his body other than the hands. Thus, he can be asked to tap it with his head, hips, knees, or feet.

Other variations can be introduced by giving the child an extension of the hand, such as a bat or a racket. He can then be asked to bat a ball or a floating balloon. When rackets are used, the badminton bird is frequently a useful object since it floats slowly and follows a somewhat irregular course.

In the area of propulsion, the child should be encouraged to exert force on an object which will move, and he should follow after it as it moves away. Here, again, the most common objects used are balls. The child should learn to kick the ball with either foot and with varying degrees of force. He should be encouraged to observe the relationships between his activity and the movement of the ball, both in terms of direction of movement and in terms of extent and rate of movement.

When the hands and arms are used instead of the feet, the activity is one of throwing. The child should learn to throw the ball with either hand or with both hands. He should throw it in front of him, to the side of him, above him, and below him. In the throwing activity the synchrony of release becomes important. In order to develop a good throw, the child must release the ball at the proper point in the movement. It is often necessary to go back and give attention to the problem of release when teaching the child to throw.

When the child has learned to throw in various directions and with various degrees of force, a target should be introduced. The child should be asked to alter the direction and force of his motor activity in terms of a distant visual target. Targets in the nature of containers, which will trap the object and thereby give immediate knowledge of results, are the most useful. The target not only calls the child's attention to the skill of the throwing pattern but also encourages him to observe the movement of the object in space after it is thrown. When the child has learned to manipulate balls and similar objects which are relatively easy to throw and whose course is relatively predictable, irregular objects should be introduced. Such things as bean bags, discs, light weight objects (such as feathers or cotton balls), objects with a minimum roll or slide (such as rubber horseshoes) should be experimented with. Variation can be introduced by giving the child an extension of the hand (such as those used in soccer or shuffleboard) with which to propel the object. The relationship between propulsion and locomotion can be illustrated by asking the child to push heavy objects or objects on casters or rollers.

TEACHING LOCOMOTION

Since locomotion is a very basic pattern, and since the helplessness of the child in his environment is so obvious in the absence of the locomotor pattern, most children come to the educational system with some form of locomotion established. Most commonly this locomotor skill is that of walking. Frequently, however, this skill has been taught very specifically with the result that the child can get around by walking, but his behavior is very stilted and rigid. The skill has not been sufficiently generalized to permit him to use it for purposeful exploration of his environment. In addition, many children come to the school system with only walking as a locomotor skill, or they come with a very limited repertory of locomotor skills. The educational task then becomes twofold: (1) to establish a wider variety of locomotor skills, and (2) to increase the flexibility and variability of these skills.

The child should possess a number of locomotor skills.

Walking

Walking involves the repeated loss and recovery of balance while the body is moving in a forward direction. Balance is shifted from one leg to the other, where it is caught and held until the next step occurs. Simultaneous movements of opposite legs and arms are performed alternately. A good walk is accomplished in a smooth and regular manner, the weight shifting smoothly and easily from one foot to the other, with the forward movement being more noticeable than the vertical movement of the body. The heel should contact the ground first, and the weight should rock forward to the ball of the foot.

Running

Running differs from walking in two ways. In the run, the body is out of contact with the ground for a short period of time during each step, whereas in walking either one foot or the other is always in contact with the ground. The ball of the foot touches the ground first on each step in running, whereas the heel makes contact first in walking. In running, the body is inclined forward from the ankles, the inclination being greater as the speed of the run increases. The arms are held relatively high and ahead of the body with the elbows slightly bent. Flow of movement from one side of the body to the other should be smooth, even, and rhythmical. The child should be able to run at various speeds, adapting the rhythm and length of stride to the requirement of the task.

Jumping

The jump is a locomotor pattern in which the knees, ankles, and hips are bent and then forcefully extended to project the body into the air in a vertical or a forward direction, or both. The child should be able to project the body above the surface of the ground with either one foot or both feet propelling the weight. If both legs are used, the action of the two legs should be simultaneous and equal. If one leg is used, the child should be able to maintain balance during the takeoff on one foot and regain it after the landing.

Crawling

Crawling is a four-point gait on hands and knees. First one hand, then the opposite knee; the other hand, and its opposite knee are lifted successively from the ground and placed in a forward position. The weight of the body is alternately transferred first to one hand, then opposite leg, then the other hand, and opposite leg as each in turn comes in contact with the ground. The movement of each limb is a forward one with shoulder or hip raised sufficiently at each stride to allow the part to clear the floor. Crawling is an important locomotor skill because it involves the coordinated activity of all four quadrants of the body in succession.

Skipping

Skipping is a modification of the walk or run in which emphasis is placed on the smooth flow of weight distribution from one side of the body to the other. Skipping involves an alternate one-footed jump or hop in a forward direction, the pace of alternation from one side to the other being primarily determined by the momentum of the forward movement. The child should be able to skip smoothly and freely. The weight should shift without apparent interruption from one side to the other. Both sides should perform normally and equally, and a definite rhythm should be maintained throughout the activity.

Galloping

The gallop is a run in which the activity does not shift alternately from one side to the other. One leg is used as a lead or landing part, and the other is used as a push or propelling part. Galloping requires the child to give up the customary pattern of alternation and to use one side as a consistent lead-side. He should be able to gallop with either a right-foot-lead ar a left-foot-lead.

Although the above is not an exhaustive list of locomotor activities, it is thought to include the most important skills which the child should possess. An attempt should be made early in the child's training to determine whether or not he is capable of performing each of these activities. If he is not, effort should be made to teach him.

The most desirable method of teaching is demonstration. The teacher goes through for the child the movement which is being taught, and the child attempts to imitate this movement. Since, as we shall see later, experimentation and generalization are extremely important aspects of the locomotor activity, it is desirable for the child to *experiment* immediately in an attempt to imitate the demonstrated pattern. We should not be too quick to break the activity into segments with attempts to develop skill in the individual segments. It is preferable in the beginning to permit the child to experiment freely with the total pattern of activity. Later, if there is a segment with which he is having particular difficulty, it may be desirable to "break out" this segment and more directly structure his movements. His overall progress, however, will be increased if he can be brought to work out, through his own experimentation, his difficulties with specific segments of the activity.

Many children will be found, however, to require additional information in order to work out a pattern. Through demonstration, information is presented visually. This visual information will frequently not be enough to permit the child to perform. Therefore, it may be necessary to put the child through the activity in order to add tactual and kinesthetic information to the visual information. The provision of such additional information involves moving the limb or part to the position where it should be. Thus, if the child is having difficulty coordinating the two sides of the body in the crawling activity, it may be necessary to grasp the knee on one side of the body and the wrist on the other side of the body to move them into the desired positions. The emphasis here should be on the additional tactual and kinesthetic clues, and the child should be encouraged to observe the position of the limbs and the method by which they arrived at this position. As soon as the child has learned the specific movements involved in a locomotor skill, emphasis should immediately be shifted to smooth, even, and rhythmical performance.

It will be noted that all of the described activities involve a flow of movement from one side of the body to the other with a concomitant shift of balance and weight from one side to the other. Difficulty in an even flow across the midline of the body or a hesitancy or jerky performance in shifting weight and balance from one side to the other is frequently associated with difficulties in laterality. Laterality is the appreciation within the body of the difference between the right side and the left and of the difference between activities on the two sides of the body. This laterality is a very important concept which the child must develop since it will later become the basis for the projection of directional relationships onto outside objects.[3] Experimentation with the flow of movement in locomotor activities can contribute markedly to the child's development of the concept of laterality.

Variation

If the child is to use locomotor activities for the purpose of exploring the environment surrounding him, these activities must be flexible and variable. Most children will be able to move the body through space. However, many children will be found in whom this movement is stilted and rigid. Such children are unable to adapt their movements to the demands of the environment, but must limit themselves to those environmental explorations which can be adapted to their rigid patterns of locomotion. It is obvious that for such children, exploration will be limited. Attention, which should be directed towards the exploratory activities, will need to be diverted to the problem of making the exploratory movements. Consequently, one of the major educational problems is to teach the child flexibility in locomotion. He should learn a *motor generalization* which will permit him to move in any direction or in any pattern to accomplish the task at hand. The problem of movement should become so elaborated and integrated that it operates as a total function subserving environmental interactions. The child should progress from a collection of locomotor skills to a locomotor generalization which will permit him on the one hand to concretely explore his environment, and on the other hand, through motor manipulation, to categorize and integrate the information obtained by such exploration.

Such variation of locomotor skills can be promoted through classroom activities. It is obvious that attention will need to be given to the problem of variation itself. The child has encountered some sort of difficulty in learning motor skills and activities which are common to the normal child. Because of this difficulty, the extensive motor experimentation which the normal child uses has been avoided by the handicapped child because, for him, the probabilities of failure are greater. Through a constant avoidance of such extensive motor experimentation, he has failed to gather the necessary data to make the generalization which would develop naturally in the normal child. Generalization develops only out of variation and experimentation. It involves the derivation of a principle from particulars. Such a derivation is impossible unless the particulars are experienced. In the motor area, such particulars are variations in specific motor acts.

There are many general methods by which such experimentation can be encouraged. Although they are discussed here under the pattern of locomotion because they can be seen more clearly in this area, they also apply to all other motor-pattern areas discussed.

MAKING VARIATION THE OBJECT OF THE ACTIVITY

Activities can be designed in which variation is demanded and in which the success of the activity depends upon the ability to vary. The simplest of such activities is a tumbling mat laid down on the floor. The child is brought to one end of the mat and is given the simple instruction to "get to the other side of the mat." He is allowed to traverse the mat in any manner which he chooses. Normally, of course, he will first walk across the mat. He is then asked to return using another method. It is pointed out to him that he walked across the first time, now he must return using some other method. Normally, he can be expected to run back. The second instruction is then repeated, "go back across, using another method." This activity is repeated in the same fashion, the child being required to use as many locomotor skills as possible.

The child may be expected to show three approaches, in order, to such a problem. First, he will run through those locomotor skills which are familiar to him and in which he has relatively high degrees of skill. Second, he will develop minor changes on one or more of these highly skilled activities. Thus, he may walk across with one hand held above his head, then he may walk across with his hands held behind his back. A large number of minor variations on a familiar skill will be used. In the last stage, when he has begun to run out of such variations, he will actively experiment with new methods of locomotion or with extensive changes in previous methods. It is this third stage of activity which represents the greatest learning situation for the child.

Each child should be permitted to run through all three of these stages a few times. It is only through such an inventory that he can be made aware of what his locomotor skills are and the extent to which he can use them. However, if the activity is prolonged in its present form beyond the stage of such an inventory, much valuable learning time will be lost as the child repeats over and over the activities of phase two. He will spend a major portion of the allotted time running through a series of minor and, at this point, insignificant changes on an already established skill. To avoid this prolonged second stage and to induce more active experimentation, the activity can be altered into a form of the old game, "follow the leader." In this modification the children are taught in groups. The first child in line is asked to cross the mat, and each child is asked to imitate his method. On the second round, the second child in line becomes the leader and each child is required to imitate his method, and so on. In this modification each child will, as before, build changes on his most adequate skill. However, in a group of children many different kinds of skills will be represented. Therefore, each child will be building modifications around a different basic skill, and the other children will be asked to imitate. Therefore, for the remainder of the group, more active experimentation is required.

It should be pointed out that the motor acts which may be involved in such a game are not as limited as might at first be thought. We should not be content with only four or five methods of traversing the mat. There are at least forty-eight different recorded methods of moving the body across a tumbling mat. The child should be able to use a majority of these many methods.

CHANGING SURROUNDING CONDITIONS

Situations can be devised in which the conditions surrounding an activity are altered. Such alteration can take a number of forms. Perhaps the easiest to approach is that of *altering the effect of the force of gravity.* This can be done by giving the child weights to carry or by asking him to perform with sand bags attached to his limbs. If these weights are applied symmetrically, the overall effect is merely to increase the force of gravity. If they are applied asymmetrically, the effect is to distort the force of gravity. In a swimming pool, the force of gravity is altered through the buoyancy of the water. In addition to buoyancy, any movement of the body or a part of the body is altered by virtue of the increased resistance of the water as opposed to the resistance of the air. Therefore, in a swimming pool, in addition to the swimming skill itself, such activities as walking through the water, standing in water of various depths, and experimenting with familiar movements in this new element can be important teaching devices. The child's attention should be called to the alteration of the effect of gravity and to the necessary alterations in movements required to counteract or compensate for these alterations rather than being exclusively directed toward the development of water skills.

The trampoline and other devices by which the child is thrown into the air represent an alteration in the effect of gravity. For a fraction of a second the child is suspended in the air, and the force of gravity is counteracted. Balance and postural adjustments must be made and maintained in the face of this counteraction of the normal effect of gravity. Walking about on the bed of the trampoline, where the spring of the canvas alternately emphasizes and counteracts the response to gravity, provides good opportunity for the child to experiment with his movement patterns in the face of altered surrounding conditions. Later, bouncing and simple stunts on the trampoline can emphasize such learnings.

Moving over irregular terrain, such as walking up and down hills, stairs, and ramps emphasizes alteration in the effect of the force of gravity. The child is required to experiment and to adjust his movement skills to the distortion in the method of application of gravity represented under these conditions.

Conditions can also be introduced which alter the nature of the contact of the body with the surface of the earth. Thus, the child can walk on ice or a slippery surface in which the friction at the point of contact is reduced, or he can walk on rough or irregular surfaces, such as in sand or on cobblestone where the friction is increased and the nature of the contact is irregular. In activities involving hand contact, various media such as finger paints, crayons, or chalk on chalkboard can be used to vary the relationship between activity and the surface. Such variations require the child to adjust his movements to differences in the nature and effect of the contact with the surface of the earth or object in his environment.

The child can also be asked to perform under varying conditions of force or leverage. Thus, the activity can be designed so that he is requested to voluntarily alter the force of his movement. He can be asked to kick an object easily or to kick it hard; he can be asked to stamp his feet as he walks; he can be asked to throw easily or to throw hard.

Activities can be designed in which the limbs, particularly the arms and legs, can be altered in length, bulk, or number. Thus the child can learn to walk on stilts. He can reach and contact an object with a pole or wand. The bulk of the feet or hands can be increased by wrapping them in burlap or by walking while wearing devices such as swim fins. The number of limbs involved in an activity can be decreased, as when the child is asked to hop on one foot or crawl on three legs. They can be increased as in the three-legged walk and similar games.

Interference with Movement

During any activity, external interference can be introduced. Thus, when a child is walking, he can be pushed or shoved slightly to throw him out of balance. This interference temporarily disrupts the walking pattern. The child is required to get back in pattern with as little interruption as possible. Of course, the situation should be designed so that such interference is expected and is a part of the game, rather than its being introduced suddenly or in a manner which can be interpreted as punitive. The normal rough-and-tumble activities of children in small groups can often be encouraged for this value as interference with set patterns of motor response.

In like manner the child can be asked to interrupt his own task. Thus, he can be asked to change direction upon verbal command; he can be asked to change force or speed upon command. For example, in the walking pattern, a series of commands can be given: *turn right, turn left, run, stop.* Emphasis should be placed upon the efficiency and speed with which the pattern can be altered to satisfy the command. The child should be able to alter his action without the necessity of waiting until he can "think out" the necessary alteration before performing. He should be able to alter smoothly and immediately without apparent interruption. The commands should be delivered in random order at unpredictable times. The greatest learning activity involves the adjustment to an unexpected command. Therefore, if the command is predictable, much of the opportunity for learning is eliminated.

We can interfere with the child's pattern by interposing obstacles. Thus, an obstacle course may be worked out requiring the child to veer around objects, climb over objects, crawl under objects, and alter length or direction of stride. Stepping stones or similar activities can be used to force alterations in pattern as the child proceeds through an activity.

Another interference which can demand experimentation is that of pacing. The child can be asked to alter his activity in relation to a rhythm which is imposed from outside. Such pacing is frequently done verbally. It can also be done visually, as when the child is asked to imitate a movement he sees which varies in pace. It can also be done mechanically as when two children turn a jump rope and one child is required to adjust his activity to the pace of the other as it is transmitted through the movement of the rope.

The important aspect of gross motor training for educational purposes is the development of the motor generalization. Therefore, it is important that one or more of these forms of variation be introduced as soon as possible. When the child has developed sufficient skill to be able to perform the task, variation should be introduced immediately. The development of high degrees of specific skills should be avoided, and emphasis should be placed on the development of the generalization. Variation is essential. When the child has achieved a high degree of skill, such variation interferes with quality of performance. The child will resent this interference. Therefore, the most efficient time to introduce variation, both from the point of view of the child and from the point of view of the learning, is immediately upon the development of sufficient skill to permit any performance in the task.

GENERALIZATION

As has been pointed out above, the primary problem in the teaching of the child with a perceptual-motor handicap is that of developing generalization. This child, because of his difficulty, will find it easier to develop a specific skill than to develop a generalization. Therefore, in all of the activities discussed above, care must be taken to encourage generalization as opposed to the development of a specific skill.

The problem of generalization determines how the task will be set for the child. The more structured the directions for the task, the more the child is encouraged toward specific skill and the less toward generalization. Therefore, tasks should be presented in stages varying from complete lack of structure to high degrees of structure. The first presentation of any task should be made as unstructured as possible. Thus, if we wish to teach climbing and we are asking the child to climb over an obstacle, the first instruction would be, "can you get across?" This instruction is as little structured as possible. The child is not told how to get across. He is not given any clues as to the particular skill or movement to be used. The only portion of the task which is structured is the final goal. The child should be encouraged to attempt the task with no further structuring.

If he has made an attempt and has been unsuccessful, the second stage of instruction is used. This is the stage of demonstration. The instructor performs the act and asks the child to imitate it. In this stage, some structuring is presented. However, it is not specific and the child is required to translate what he has seen into movements of his body.

If he is unsuccessful in imitation, then the task may be structured for him. His limbs may be moved through the stages of the task, and he may be told what movements to make at each step. This high degree of structuring should be used only as a last resort. In this stage, we have given the child a specific series of movements. If he is having difficulty in the problem of generalization, he will tend to learn these movements in this specific fashion.

Any new task should be introduced in stage one. Stage two and three should be employed only if necessary. As soon as the child has successfully completed a task, he should immediately be asked to see if he can do it in a different way. Variation and generalization should be encouraged at all points.

THE CHILD WITH A MOTOR DEFECT

A word is in order at this point concerning the child who has a specific motor defect. Most obvious among such children are the cerebral-palsied whose brain damage has interfered with the neurological impulses innervating muscles or muscle systems. Since such defects are of neurological origin, they are constant. Any movement or pattern of movements involving the affected muscles will be disrupted in the same manner. The defect is predictable; there is no variation. Whenever the affected muscle is involved, the defect will be present.

Because of the constancy and the predictability of this specific motor defect, it does not represent a basic interference with the motor pattern. Motor patterns can be built around the defect and, since the defect is constant, compensations for its effect can be developed. It is as though in the development of any motor pattern, the child simply computes a formula for the movement, then adds a constant to compensate for the defect and uses this constant in all of the formulas involving this pattern.

The compensation for the specific defect will usually involve a distortion of the motor pattern. This distortion, however, can also be constant and can be predicted in any use made of the pattern. As with the normal motor pattern, this distorted pattern can become flexible and attention can be directed from the motor movement itself to the object of the movement. Thus, the distorted pattern of the cerebral-palsied child can serve the same function in the same manner that the more typical pattern of the normal child serves.

There is, however, a secondary problem with the specific motor defect which often causes trouble. Because a muscle or a set of muscles is disturbed, certain activities involving this group of muscles will be difficult for the child and will involve a high probability of failure. The child will tend, therefore, to avoid these types of activities. As a result of this avoidance, there will develop around these specific defects an area of secondary defects resulting from inadequate learning. Because the child has avoided an area of activity, he has deprived himself of the learning experiences necessary to develop responses in that area. Around the basic motor defect, he now has a *halo* of secondary defect resulting from inadequate experimentation and learning.

This halo is not constant. The difficulties are not neurological in origin, and consequently they are not predictable. Muscles involved in the activities of the halo will sometimes respond and will sometimes not respond, depending upon the total pattern of stimulation and response of the moment. Because of this unpredictability, the secondary defects cannot be accounted for by compensation. No constant can be developed that can be inserted into the formula of movement patterns to account for these inconstant defects. The situation in the area of the halo therefore becomes similar to the situation with the child who has not learned adequate motor patterns in the first place. The difficulties tend to become cumulative since activities involving responses near the present halo area now become difficult and their failure-probability is increased due to the halo. This new area of difficulty then suffers from learning restrictions and eventually is added to the halo. By such a cumulative process, the halo increases as the child develops and as he encounters more and more areas of difficulty.

Where such halo effects are present, the child's difficulties are similar to those of the child who lacks motor patterns initially. The problem of teaching must involve reduction of the halo. Activities which lie at the outside edge of the halo will need to be prescribed. The child must be encouraged to develop and elaborate these marginal responses. By such practice, the halo can be slightly reduced. Teaching should then move to an area somewhat closer to the specific defect, thereby reducing the halo again. This process of gradual movement toward the area of performance directly affected neurologically will need to be continued until the child's responses have been brought to the point where the true defect is encountered. At this point no further movement will be possible for the child, and his responses will take the form of compensation and distortion rather than more normal learning.

When the halo has been reduced to the point where the specific defect is the major effect demaining, the interference with behavior will become constant. At this point, the child should be encouraged to develop adequate compensation for the necessary distortions in behavior and these distorted patterns should be accepted since, as we noted above, they are now consistent and will not interfere with subsequent learning activities. It seems possible that much of the reported reduction in overt evidences of cerebral palsy has been due, not so much to an alteration of the basic defect, as to a reduction in the extent of halo.

THE PERCEPTUAL-MOTOR MATCH

Although the initial responses of the infant are motor responses, he begins almost immediately to respond to perceptual stimulation as well. The period of motor development and the period of perceptual development are much more overlapping than they are discrete. As was indicated earlier, meaningfulness is imposed upon perceptual stimulation through motor manipulation and through the observation of the perceptual data, along with changes in these data as motor manipulations occur. This combination of motor data and perceptual data begins almost as soon as the initial motor responses become operative. The process of combining perceptual information and motor information into a meaningful whole has been called the perceptual-

motor match. Perceptual data must be matched to motor information in order to make them meaningful. If such a match is not
made, the child comes to live in two worlds; one in which he sees,
hears, and feels, and another in which he responds with overt
movement. If these two areas of experience are not welded together through the perceptual-motor match, constant confusion
results. Therefore, it is necessary to introduce perceptual training
along with motor training from the very initial stages of teaching
in the case of a child with a perceptual-motor handicap.

It will be noted that in the activities already discussed, perceptual data have constantly been introduced into the activities.
Thus, when we ask a child to walk along a walking board, we ask
him to orient visually to the board and to use this visual information along with the motor information as he performs. When we
are teaching the skills of receipt and propulsion, a perceptual
target is introduced as soon as possible. Thus the child is encouraged to move as soon as he can from merely throwing a ball to
throwing a ball at a target or into a container. It is necessary to
introduce such perceptual factors as early as possible in training
and to consistently call the child's attention to the relationship
between the perceptual data and the motor data.

In the very early stages of the development of the perceptual-
motor match, the motor aspect is predominant. Initially, the hand
guides the eye. The hand makes the first meaningful contact with
the object, and the eye is brought to the point of hand contact.
In this sense the eye-hand relationship is dominated by the motor
response of the hand. Since perceptual data are so much more
efficient and so much more extensive both in space and time than
motor activities, the situation quickly reverses. Now the eye
guides the hand because of its greater flexibility. In the normal
child, this second stage of eye-hand coordination develops so rapidly that the initial motor-dominated stage is frequently overlooked.
As with so many developmental processes, the two aspects of eye-
hand coordination are more overlapping than they are discrete.
Thus, as soon as the hand can guide the eye adequately in a given
activity, the child tends to shift to the second phase in which the
eye guides the hand. At the same time, in more complex activities

he may be operating at the first stage. Therefore, it is frequently difficult to separate the two aspects. In learning a new or complex task, the child frequently must go back and repeat these two approaches. Training activities should therefore be designed to permit the hand to guide the eye but at the same time to encourage the shift as soon as possible to perceptual control.

There would appear to be three stages in the development of the perceptual-motor match: (1) control of single acts, (2) control of continuous activities, and (3) control of sequential acts. In most cases the perceptual-motor match will be found to develop through these three stages in order.

Perceptual-Motor Control of Single Acts

The control of a single act involves the perceptual identification of a point in space and the motor act of bringing the body or a part of the body to that point through a single simple movement. Thus, if we ask the child to step on a square of colored paper pasted on the floor, we ask him first to identify the location of the paper through perceptual data and then to perform a movement that will bring his foot into contact with the paper. We require perceptual identification of a point in space and emphasize the perceptual control and encourage the relationship of perceptual to motor data when we ask him to step on the goal. He must be encouraged to look at the square first and to put his foot where he is looking. In the very early stages or with highly disturbed children, a child may step without looking. (If so, he should be asked to see whether or not he has stepped on the square.) In this case the motor has come first and the perceptual later. The child is behaving in the first stage of the perceptual-motor match described above. He should be encouraged to move as soon as possible to the second stage of looking first and then using these perceptual data to control his motor response.

Many common materials and activities can be used as training devices in this area. Thus, the pegboard will be found useful. At this stage we are not interested in the pegboard as a device for encouraging form perception, we are simply interested in it as a device for perceptual-motor manipulation. The child is first asked to take a peg, which is held in the teacher's hand. Again, he is encouraged to look at the peg and move his hand directly to it; he is discouraged from moving his hand aimlessly until contact with the peg is made. When he has grasped the peg, he is asked to put it in the board. No restriction is placed on this activity. He is not told where to put it but only to find a hole and fit it in. At a somewhat later stage in training, the difficulty can be increased by pointing to a specific hole and requiring the child to place his peg in this prescribed hole. At a still later stage, a hole can be prescribed visually. Thus, pegs can be placed around a single hole so that there is one empty hole in the middle of a group of pegs. The child can then be asked to place his peg in the vacant hole. Here the perceptual problem has been increased since he must sort out from a number of perceptual data the one or ones pertinent to his immediate problem.

The same activities described earlier, in which objects are placed in containers, can be used to further the perceptual-motor match. Previously, we were interested in the child's grasp, his maintenance of contact with the object, and his ability to release it. In the present connection, interest centers on the perceptual-motor relationship. The child will be encouraged to identify the goal and use this perception to control the motor act. Emphasis will be placed upon directness of response and upon certainty and precision in the motor act.

Many common materials and activities can be used to teach the perceptual-motor control of single acts. In most cases, however, emphasis needs to be shifted from a concern with the product which the child achieves, to a concern with the method by which he achieves this product. Thus, the stacking of blocks can teach perceptual-motor control if attention is shifted from the construction to the method of placing each block. Thus, in the present context, interest would be centered on how accurately and how assuredly the child can place each block. In similar manner, Tinker toys℗ can be used. Here, interest is centered on the manner in which a child places a stick in a knob. Sewing cards and similar materials are useful, but concern is centered on the accuracy with which the child inserts the needle into the opening. Many kinds of materials involve the placing of forms or similar abstract materials on dowels of ropes. These materials are useful in the present context if attention is given, not to the child's selection of a form, but to his method of placing the form on the dowel or string.

Perceptual-Motor Control of Continuous Activities

When the child can control a single act by the use of perceptual data, he can be asked to control a continuous motor act. In this situation, he must use changing perceptual data to continuously monitor an ongoing motor response. Such control is of particular importance in education because of its significance in all types of pencil and paper activities. Such activities require the child to produce a continuous movement which varies in direction or speed. He must also maintain a constant control of this movement on the basis of the perceptual data which are being produced. Whereas, in the case of the single act, one perceptual contact could be used to control the entire process; in the case of a continuous activity, perceptual contact must be maintained, and the perceptual-motor relationship cannot be sporadic.

In the early stages of the development of control of continuous acts, the chalkboard will be found a better training device than paper or pencil. Because of its size and its vertical orientation, experimentation with larger movements is possible, and the demands for precision in muscular control are less with the chalkboard. In addition, directions with the chalkboard are reality-oriented rather than symbolic. Thus, the direction *up* is away from the surface of the earth on the chalkboard; it is away from the body, but parallel to the surface of the earth on pencil and paper. For these reasons it will usually be found desirable to begin training in the area of continuous activity with chalkboard tasks.

The simplest controlled activity on the chalkboard is that of tracing. The child is asked to control his motor response in terms of perceptual data which remain available to him. If perceptual contact is suspended momentarily, the data necessary to "get back on the track" are present as soon as contact is re-established. In the more complex activities of drawing and copying, which will come later, the necessary perceptual data are not continuously present. Therefore, tracing is an excellent initial activity since it provides additional perceptual cueing when it is needed.

Tracing activities should begin with simple straight lines in vertical and horizontal directions. The lines should not be too long so that the requirement of continuous control is too great, and the markings to be traced should be wide enough so that the requirements for precise control are reduced. As the child learns control, the length of the lines can be increased and their width can be decreased, thus encouraging longer periods of consistent control and greater precision of control. Curved lines and closed figures can then be introduced. The child should not be allowed to move randomly back and forth across a line but should be encouraged to control his movements by the perceptual data. Thus, he should trace rather slowly, and it should be assured that he is attending perceptually to the material being traced.

More continuous control over longer periods can be encouraged by asking the child to trace over and over a closed figure. The most convenient figure is the circle since the rhythm of the movement is not interrupted in this task. The child is asked to go around and around the figure, staying on the line. Upon command, he is asked to reverse direction and go the other way. He is encouraged to attend to both the perceptual and motor data at all times.

Activities on both sides of the body can be compared if the child is asked to perform this task with both hands at once. Thus, he may be asked to trace over two circles at once, one on his right with his right hand and one on his left with his left hand. Attention should be directed to the perceptual data from both circles. He must be watched to see that the two circles are approximately the same size and shape and that the two hands are traveling at the same speed so that their actions are synchronized. Thus, when the child's right hand arrives at the top of the right circle, his left hand should arrive at the top of the left circle. This activity is very useful in encouraging the child to compare the two sides of the body and the similarities and differences between actions on the two sides. Upon command, he should change direction in the following patterns: (1) right hand counterclockwise, left hand clockwise; (2) right hand clockwise, left hand counterclockwise; (3) both hands counterclockwise; (4) both clockwise.

Drawing activities require the child to control his movements on the basis of perceptual data which are being produced in the course of the activity. Thus, the perceptual data created by the initial movement are used to determine the subsequent movement. Drawing activities with straight vertical and horizontal lines should be introduced first. Diagnoal lines are more difficult and should not be introduced until later. The child should not be allowed to run his hand aimlessly back and forth. He should be given the prescribed task of drawing a line and should be encouraged to attend to the perceptual information, using this to control his act. He should draw vertical lines in a downward direction and also in an upward direction. Horizontal lines should be drawn from left to right and also from right to left.

A child will learn to mark without confinement before he will learn to mark within the confines of lines. Much of the later activity prescribed by the educational program will require the child to confine his drawings within the limits of a piece of paper or within the limits of lines on a piece of paper. Therefore, he should begin learning early to confine his activities within prescribed areas.

One of the initial approaches to the limitation represented by a prescribed space is asking the child to complete a ladder drawn on the chalkboard. Two vertical lines representing the uprights of the ladder are drawn. The child is then asked to draw in the rungs. These are horizontal lines beginning at one upright and ending at the other. The child should be encouraged to pay attention first to the beginning point at one vertical line and then to the ending point at the other vertical line, as well as to the control of his production between these two points. He should not be permitted to mark randomly between the verticals but should be urged to control the entire act by use of perceptual data.

When the child has obtained some control over the straight-line drawing task, curves can be introduced. Three patterns can be suggested in the development of the drawing of curves, (1) the simple arc of the circle, with a single direction of movement maintained (A in Fig. 1); (2) a curve with a change of direction involved, as from vertical to right-hand movement (E in Fig. 1); (3) tasks with complete change of direction involved, as up to down (G in Fig. 1).

It will be found that the drawing of curves can be learned more easily if the sequence of introducing the various directions represented in Figure 1 is followed. In general, the child learns movements away from the median axis of the body more easily than movements toward the median axis of the body (A and B). In like manner, the smooth curves in A will be learned more readily than the sharper curves in E which, in turn, will be learned more readily than the complete change of direction represented by G and J.

When the child has experimented with these simple drawing tasks on the chalkboard, they can be transferred to paper. In making this transfer, care should be taken to avoid an abrupt transition. Thus, the child may be given large sheets of paper such as newsprint and may be permitted to use the same large movements that he used on the chalkboard, before he is asked to confine his activities to the smaller spaces represented by the lines on writing paper, which will be his guides in the more complex activities to follow.

Copying activities require the child to interpret perceptual data in motor terms, to carry out the motor activities, and subsequently to check the product perceptually. When material to be copied is placed before the child, he must first examine it perceptually. These perceptual data are then interpreted in terms of the types of motor movement which will produce similar data. When the necessary movements have been accomplished, the child checks his result against the copy again. The entire process thus involves first a perceptual interpretation, then a motor response, and finally a perceptual-matching activity. Copying is more difficult than random drawing because the actions are more strictly prescribed. If the child is asked to draw a curved line, for example, he may produce any one of a number of reasonable approximations to a curve. If he is asked to copy a square, however, the amount of variation permitted is greatly reduced. Thus the requirements of the perceptual-motor match are much more rigid in the case of copying than in the case of random drawing.

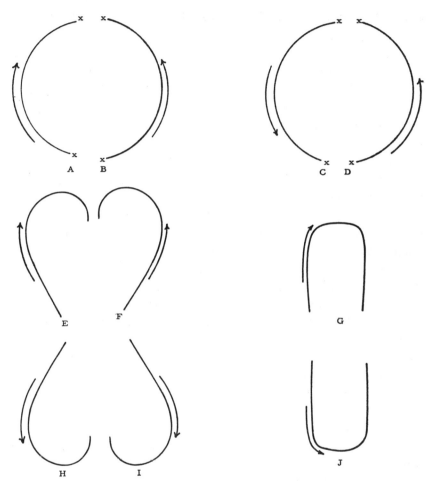

FIGURE 1. Sequences of direction of movement in teaching curved lines.

Copying activity should begin with simple geometric forms. Developmentally, the first of these forms to appear is the circle. The circular form is followed in order by the cross, the square, the triangle, the rectangle, and finally the diamond. Templets may be used to aid the child where necessary, and tracing activities may be introduced as intermediate steps. Detailed descriptions of copying activities have been presented elsewhere.[3]

Perceptual-Motor Control of Sequential Acts

For the child, sequential activities are a combination of continuous activity and single acts. The overall activity of the sequence is continuous, but each step must be broken out as a single act. In the process of performing the single act, the continuity of the total sequence must not be lost. The perceptual-motor demands made by sequential activities are therefore greater than those of either a continuous activity or an individual act.

Many of the tasks presented to children in the school curriculum represent such sequential acts. The reading process, for example, involves the consideration of a prescribed sequence of perceptual data *in order*. In a single fixation, the eyes provide data concerning the first section of a line of print. When this section has been dealt with, the eyes move on to the next section, which in turn is dealt with. The reading process demands that these portions be dealt with in order, and that the continuity of the total process be maintained while each portion is considered individually. The orderly progress of the child through a series of items in a workbook is a similar sequential act; the acting out of a story and the recounting of a series of events represent illustrations of other sequential acts. Many of the activities used in the classroom situation demand perceptual-motor control of sequential acts.

It will be seen that before the child is ready to control a sequence of acts, he must be able to control not only a single act but also a continuous activity. The controls discussed above therefore should be reasonably well-established in the child before sequential activities are introduced. Many of the difficulties encountered by a handicapped child in ordinary classroom tasks will be traced to the fact that sequential activities have been prescribed for the child before he has established necessary control of basic activity.

Training in dealing with sequences should involve both the

concrete level and the symbolic level. At the concrete level, the child is asked to manipulate concrete objects in a serial order. Such activities as stringing beads to produce a design by the sequential addition of various colors or shapes can provide such training. The common nested cup sets, in which cups varying in size must be placed inside each other in order of their size, can also be used. The child can be asked to duplicate designs produced by a line of blocks varying in color or size. With a pegboard, the child can be asked to fill the holes in a prescribed order, or he can create designs of a sequential nature with pegs of different colors.

In more symbolic activities, the tasks represented by kindergarten and prekindergarten workbooks often involve sequential activities. Thus, matching tasks, in which a picture on one side of the page is joined by a line to the same picture on the other side of the page, present a sequence problem. The child must deal with the picture on the one side of the page while he deals with those on the opposite side of the page in a different but related sequence.

OCULAR CONTROL

A very large number of tasks, which are presented to the child in the classroom, require vision as a primary avenue of perceptual input. For this reason, vision becomes one of the most important sensory areas for education. Visual perception is complicated by the motility of the eyes within the head. The eye can be moved so that it points in any of a number of directions. The direction in which it is pointed will determine the visual information which is obtained. Such movement of the eye is controlled by six extraocular muscles which act to alter the position of the eye in its socket. The control of these extraocular muscles is a neuromuscular skill and, as such, it must be learned just as the control of the hand or the control of any other body part must be learned. The learning involved in control of the eye is complicated by the fact that the criterion for the adequacy of control is the perceptual input itself. The primary method by which we know the eye is properly pointed is through observation of the visual information.

If we are seeing what we are supposed to be looking at, we know the eye is pointed in the right direction. Kinesthetic information from the extraocular muscles and other clues help us to determine the line of sight, but our major dependence is upon the visual input. Particularly for checking or refined correction, we rely heavily upon the perceptual input for control of the ocular positioning.

However, if ocular control is not established, the input cannot be established either. If there is no consistent control of the eye, the visual input must be similarly inconsistent; it cannot then be used as a dependable control device, and the entire system breaks down. Therefore, until control is accomplished, the child does not have the criterion to evaluate his control. The awareness of degree of control is, as it were, after the fact, and the child must learn to control the neuromuscular apparatus in terms of, and in relation to, the perceptual input which results from this control.

Many children, and particularly children in whom perceptual-motor relationships are not strong, will display inadequate control of the extraocular muscles. As a result, the visual input is not constant and perceptual-motor matching becomes more difficult. It is frequently necessary, therefore, to provide such children specific training in the control of the eye. Ocular control involves two problems. The first of these is maintaining the eye in a fixed position until the necessary perceptual information has been obtained. The second problem involves maintaining visual contact with a moving object, or moving the eye sequentially among a series of objects, obtaining the necessary information throughout the entire process. The first of these problems requires training in ocular fixation. The second requires training in ocular pursuit.

Fixation

Visual fixation means maintaining visual contact with a stationary object for a period of time sufficient to gather the necessary information for perceptual interpretation. A child who cannot hold a visual fixation for a reasonable period of time cannot maintain contact long enough to gather necessary perceptual data.

Training in this skill involves rather direct practice in holding visual fixation.

Hold a visual target in each hand before the child. (Suitable targets might be any small objects which are interesting to the child.) The objects should be held about twenty-four inches apart and roughly twenty inches in front of the child. Ask the child to look at the right-hand target. Watch his eyes. Can he point the eye directly at the target and hold it there for ten to fifteen seconds? Then ask him to look at the left hand target. Again watch his eyes. Do they shift directly to the second target, or do they "wander about" while moving to the second target? Can he hold the second target for ten to fifteen seconds? Then ask him to move back to the first target. Repeat the process asking the child to fixate and hold on each target in turn. The child should be asked to perform with each eye alone. Cover one eye and ask him to fixate with the uncovered eye. Then cover the other eye and ask him to repeat the performance. The exercise should also be performed with both eyes together.

With children who have particular difficulty, it may be desirable to use targets which, in addition to their visual stimulus value, also have an auditory stimulus value. Suitable targets would include all kinds of small noise makers such as bells, toy crickets, and clappers. The child would be asked to fixate on the target while the teacher manipulates it so that the sound is produced.

With many children it will be found that the head moves instead of the eyes. A child with this problem has not developed ocular control and is attempting to control the perceptual input by turning the head instead of turning the eyes. In this case the child's head should be held lightly so that it cannot move, and he should be encouraged to fixate with the eyes alone.

It will be found that many children perform more readily if they are permitted to use their hand as well as their eyes. These children have probably not moved from the stage, where the hand controls the eye, to the later stage, where the eye controls the hand. For these children, it is desirable to have them point to or touch the object as they look at it. When fixation is shifted from the first target to the second, they are asked to point or touch the second target as they shift their eyes to it. The target should be held in various positions so that the eye movements called for are sometimes in the vertical meridian, sometimes in the lateral meridian, and sometimes in the diagonal meridian. As in the case of the hand movements in drawing, it will be found that vertical and lateral movements are generally easier for these children than diagonal movements.

The child should learn to move the eyes from one target to another quickly, easily, and surely. The eyes should move directly to the new target without jerking or performing a series of back-and-forth approximations before accurate fixation is obtained. Once obtained, the child should also be able to hold the fixation for a reasonable period of time.

Pursuit

Training the ocular pursuit skill is similar to the fixation skill. In this case, however, one target is used, and it is moved before the child's eyes. Hold a suitable visual target about twenty inches before the eyes of the child. Ask him to watch it wherever it goes. Move the target several times in each of the following directions: lateral, vertical, diagonal, and circular. The target should be moved through a distance of twenty-four to thirty inches in each direction.

The child should be able to hold his head still and follow the target with the eyes alone. The eyes should move smoothly and maintain fixation on the target at all times. If the movement of the eyes is interrupted and the child loses visual contact with the target, stop immediately, ask him to refixate the target, and then begin the movement again. These pursuit activities should also be practiced with each eye separately and with both eyes together.

Ocular control activities are very fatiguing for the child since such control represents a difficult neuromuscular skill. Therefore, periods of practice with these tasks should be limited in length. It will generally be found that a practice period of six minutes distributed — two minutes with the left eye, two minutes with the right eye, two minutes with both eyes together — is optimal in length. The task can be repeated at a later time, but a break should occur after six minutes of such activity and the child be assigned a different task to avoid undue fatigue.

As in the activities for ocular fixation, many children will be found who will need to use a hand to aid in the control of the eye. Such children should be encouraged to point to or touch the target as it moves. When they have achieved enough skill that the eyes move smoothly and accurately in pursuit of the target, the use of the hands can be omitted.[3,4]

ADVANCED LEARNING

When the child has gained perceptual-motor skill and when he has learned the perceptual-motor control necessary to maintain consistent behavior, he can be introduced to the more complex learnings of form perception and concept formation. Details of training in these areas will not be outlined here since they have been adequately described in other literature.[1,2,5]

It will frequently be found that difficulties which the child encounters in the more complex areas of learning are owing, in part at least, to failure to lay a firm foundation in the more basic perceptual-motor skills. Thus, the child who cannot monitor a continuous activity or who cannot deal with sequential elements in a task is poorly prepared to manipulate forms and figures. The child who cannot interpret perceptual data or who cannot control his perceptual input is poorly prepared to deal with the perceptual problems of reading. The child who cannot manipulate concrete objects in a sequential fashion is poorly prepared for the symbolic manipulation of concepts. Such advanced activities will come more easily to the child and, in some cases, will become possible for the child if he is first given a firm foundation of perceptual-motor skill.

In children where perceptual-motor activities are disturbed, time spent in providing those perceptual-motor skills which are assumed by so many of our classroom tasks will be time well spent. If we can assure for these children that the assumptions of our educational system, assumptions concerning readiness skills which the child brings with him, are met, then the customary techniques of the educational system will more readily apply.

REFERENCES

1. Cruickshank, W. M.; Bentzen, F. A.; Ratzburg, R. H., and Tannhauser, M. T.: *A Teaching Method for Brain-injured and Hyperactive Children.* Syracuse, Syracuse, 1961.
2. Dunn, L. M. (Ed.) : *Exceptional Children in the Schools.* New York, Holt, 1963.
3. Kephart, N. C.: *The Slow Learner in the Classroom.* Columbus, Merrill, C. E., 1960, pp. 42-6, 183-215, 217-21, 241-57.
4. Simpson, Dorothy: Perceptual Readiness and Beginning Reading. Unpublished Doctoral Disertation, Purdue University, 1960.
5. Strauss, A. A., and Lehtinen, Laura E.: *Psychopathology and Education of the Brain-injured Child.* New York, Grune, 1947.

VIII

EDUCATIONAL METHODS BASED ON THE GELLNER CONCEPTS OF NEUROLOGICAL DEFICIT

Ruth M. Patterson

ORIENTATION

ONE OF THE MILESTONES in education of handicapped children was the delineation of the brain-injured child by Strauss and Werner in the years between 1938 and 1945.[33] Many events of importance grew from this seed. Along came the establishment of the Cove Schools at Racine, the work of Cruickshank at Syracuse, the treatment centers guided by Kephart at Purdue, numerous experimental studies,[1,2,6,8,11,19,21] and a wide recognition that behavioral reactions may result from neurological damage without any visible crippling.

The first blaze of confidence following the publications by Strauss and Lehtinen[23] and the second volume by Strauss and Kephart,[22] however, was soon dissipated in the conflicting findings of much later research. The monolithic structure of the "brain-injured child" with the endogenous versus exogenous categories in mental deficiency was further cracked by ever-growing medical discoveries which transferred small but accumulating groups from the presumably endogenous to the exogenous category. At the level of mental retardation, it became more difficult to find a valid control group for experimental purposes than to find a well-documented experimental group. Teachers and psychologists also became well-aware that many children with definite histories of brain damage did not fit the picture which came to be called the "Strauss syndrome."

In 1951, Lise Gellner, M.D., brought with her to the Columbus State School in Columbus, Ohio, a theory in regard to learning handicaps in mental deficiency. She was convinced that the efforts toward classifying mentally retarded children as brain-injured or non-brain-injured would be much better spent in identifying different types of learning and behavior deficits and demonstrating the effects of differentiated teaching methods upon them.

Dedication to this task, based upon the Gellner concepts of visual and auditory disabilities, has been the work of Research Project Number 50 of the Columbus State School for the past twelve years. In the following pages is a condensed statement of the practices in this unit and the Gellner concepts upon which they are based. Not all of Gellner's tenets have been accepted unconditionally.

THE GELLNER CONCEPTS

Much research on the functions of the midbrain and the reticular formation supports Gellner's[12] contention that pathology in these areas may be responsible for certain learning handicaps and behavioral aberrations which frequently give rise to a general picture of mental deficiency. It is the pathology, in her opinion, which is important, not the etiology behind it. Therefore, a dichotomy, such as endogenous-exogenous, is not only useless but misleading, since all mental deficiency is due to brain pathology of some kind. This view is also upheld by Pasamanick.[20] Gellner believes that the site of the lesion may be inferred from the nature of the handicap.

Among the children who come to the attention of any psychologist dealing with problems of mental development, there are a number, easily discernible, who fall into one of four types. First, there is the child who is especially inept in visual-motor activities, either large or small muscle, or both. He is apt to be slow in movement, to show no interest in constructive play or sports, and to have difficulty with number concepts. A second is the hyperactive child, often well coordinated, who fits most of the descriptive terms used by Strauss, and who is likely to have a severe reading disability. Third is the child who has difficulty in the use of language. He may or may not understand speech used by others, but he, himself, is severely limited in the production of verbal symbols. The fourth is the child who imitates the language symbols he hears with facility but has little concept of language meanings or true language communication. These four types of disability Gellner has named (1) *visual-somatic* (movement blindness); (2) *visual-autonomic* (meaning blindness); (3) *auditory-somatic* (word sound deafness); and (4) *auditory-autonomic* (word meaning deafness).

According to Gellner's theory,[12] each of these handicaps is related to pathology in a specific area of the midbrain. Behavioral anomalies which accompany these deficits may have a neurological basis or may be the psychological results of the frustrations, failures, anxieties and rejections attendant upon the lack of understanding of the child's difficulties by adults in charge of him and by his peers.

These four groups of children at the level of mental deficiency have been singled out for study by Gellner. She does not fail to recognize that known clinical types, gross physical anomalies, and extensive cortical damage are in a class apart.

Psychologists in Research Project Number 50 have set the goals of their work: (1) to show experimentally the existence of these categories of deficit,[4,5,13,14,15,16] and (2) to demonstrate through experiment, that children taught by methods appropriate to their handicaps will make better progress than will children taught by good conventional methods but without regard to the category of their deficits.

Gellner used a number of simple test devices to help her in the diagnostic appraisal of a child. These were not standardized or assigned any numerical score values, but they were used only as tools in a clinical examination by a physician. Psychologists in Project Number 50 have organized them, stabilized the materials and instructions, and they are known now as the Gellner Tests. Since the ITPA, Illinois Test of Psycholinguistic Abilities (1961), has come out, we have found that this standardized instrument, with a wider age-range, is translatable into Gellner categories. We still use the simpler Gellner tests for younger or less-capable children. A discussion of the ITPA will help to illustrate the disabilities of older children in different categories and the kinds of tasks useful in pinpointing their weaknesses.

The ITPA, built upon Osgood's (1952) theory of communication is not limited to speech. There are three types of activity postulated: (1) decoding, or the way in which sensory stimuli are interpreted (perceived) by the receiver; (2) encoding, or the skilled movements (verbal or otherwise) by which the intentions of the organism are put into messages (the means of expression); and (3) associational, or the intricate relations between the two. These processes may occur at three levels of organization: (1) the automatic, (2) the grammatical, and (3) the semantic, or concept formation.

Most important for its relation to Gellner categories is the clear-cut recognition of the auditory and visual fields in both receptive and expressive activities. For example, Test 1 explores the child's understanding of language, though he need only indicate *yes* or *no*. Test 3 requires verbal response with the already structured, correct grammatical form of the word used, while Test 5 leaves considerable latitude for voluntary language production. The visual tests range from simple recognition to visual-motor imagery and performance under visual guidance. Within the ages from two and one-half through nine and one-half years, levels of performance in these tasks have been standardized for normal children, and one may draw a profile on the record blank which highlights the areas of strength and weakness. If a deficit exists, the Gellner category can be hypothesized. A numerical score which is useful for research is also obtainable on this test.

APPLICATION OF THESE CONCEPTS TO CLASSROOM TEACHING

The efforts of the teachers in the demonstration classes of Research Project Number 50 have been to accumulate, by modification of commercial materials or construction of new ones, teaching aids and devices appropriate for each of the four categories of deficit. Gellner is most concerned with young children whose handicaps are severe. Children who reach a state institution when they are about six years of age are at a pre-readiness level; therefore, the materials and activities outlined in the manual, *Teaching*

Devices for Children with Impaired Learning (1958), are for beginners. Although the pressure for help in the public schools comes from parents and teachers of the elementary grades, leads may be found in the manual for education of the older or more able child, who may need to go back to the beginning in the area of his handicap.

Grouping of Children

Gellner advocated grouping children according to disability, so that the teaching methods used would be comprehensible to all. She thought, initially, in terms of ten children to a group. This proved unrealistic in the institution as to number of children, number of groups, and handling.

The achievement level of the children has proved a more practical grouping criterion, providing the groups are small and the teaching is individualized. As in any grouping situation, the personalities of the children are important. Since the actual attainment levels are similar, they can participate in some group activities. Each can learn to appreciate that something easy for him may be hard for another, and vice versa. The teacher must adjust the individual learning situations to each child's area of disability. The range in group size has been four to eight children, depending upon the level of the children.

Handling the Teaching Day

Children with deficits vary in their tolerance level for concentration on any given activity. It is better to have them work only as long as they can with high concentration and motivation. Half-day school sessions are often advisable, making it possible for the teacher to see eight to ten children in the course of a day. Within the half-day period, ten, fifteen, or twenty minutes may be devoted to individual training, according to the child's tolerance, while the children who are not with the teacher are doing assigned tasks. A period devoted to recreational activities has also been found helpful. (The use of records and record albums is not classified as recreational.) These are among the most useful teaching materials, as will be pointed out later.

TEACHING METHODS FOR THE GELLNER CATEGORIES

In discussing the four categories below, let us assume, for the sake of clarity, that each case is clear-cut, with no overlapping, and that the disability is nearly complete. (Such classic cases seldom turn up in the classroom, as will be discussed later.)

Visual-Somatic Children

Deficits and Strengths

These children cannot learn movements by watching. Gellner suggests that there is a lack in depth perception so that they operate in a two-dimensional world. They have no conception of trying to do something which they see someone else doing. The translation of visual stimuli into expressive action is incomprehensible to them, and they experience only frustration and negative feelings when urged to try. In large muscles, this applies to such activities as jumping, skipping, throwing or catching balls, and many other whole body movements; in small muscles, it interferes with learning to write, copying figures or patterns, drawing, and following two-dimensional black-white patterns for three-dimensional tasks, such as block building or Tinker Toys.⑦

Because of this lack of experience in the connection between visual impression and performance, the children are poor in such activities as form boards, puzzles, coloring within lines, and of course, cutting and pasting, because of the movements involved. It is small wonder that they do not succeed in kindergarten and are likely to be outsiders in the social life of their age groups.

If one explores the infantile development of these children, one usually finds that they did not *play* with their baby toys (such as hold or shake a rattle) ; they were (or perhaps still are) poor in manipulating a spoon; they did not hold or manipulate blocks nor transfer them from hand to hand; nor did they play ball. Probably they were late in walking and never learned to ride a tricycle or to handle the motor toys of childhood with much success.

On the other hand, a child of this type may have said his first word at the usual time or a little early. His language development has come along well; he likes to listen to some stories and is going through the usual stages of symbol recognition toward reading. He knows his colors and enjoys picture books. He can also count by rote quite well, and as he grows older, if someone has been teaching him that way, he even responds correctly with some memorized addition and subtraction facts. When asked to apply this knowledge in a practical situation where he has to count objects, however, he seems totally confused.

Principles for Remediation

PRE-READINESS LEVEL

The first step is to encourage the child to use his hands. They have been pretty useless appendages up to this time, and the palms may be quite sensitive. Instead of reaching out for things offered him, his tendency may be to pull his hands away. The motivation for using his hands must be supplied through pleasurable conditioning and the skill through passive training. Gellner describes cupping one's hand around that of the small child to hold a baby rattle and waving his arm to activate the tinkly bell. The teacher may help the child to splash in watery sand and to transfer fistfuls from one hand to the other, always holding his hands. Another device described by Gellner is to have little boats floating in lukewarm water in a dishpan, to help the child to load them with bright marbles until they sink, then to reach down into the water to bring them up, and then to start over. A little later, one may help the child roll clay "snakes" between his hands, and finally to pat, pound, and fashion the clay.

READINESS LEVEL

When at last the child is using his hands voluntarily in a variety of ways for simple touch and feeling sensations, one may begin to help him perceive form and shape through them. Use of a blindfold or opaque colored glasses lets him concentrate on perception through touch alone, so that he can learn to call by name *velvet,* or *sandpaper,* or *stone,* and to match and call by name forms such as circles, squares, and triangles. When he has perceived these things surely by touch and kinesthesis and the blindfold is no longer used, he has the verbal cue to help him connect his two, until now discrete, perceptive fields. Moreover, the child has been given a tool by which he can learn if he has the basic ability and insight to use it.

One must remember that these children will not be having great difficulty in connecting and remembering verbal symbols and visual word impressions — in short, reading. The reading readiness level for them can be quite conventional, involving picture recognition, picture and color and word matching, and the steps in building a sight vocabulary, so long as the visual material is two-dimensional and the response is verbal. This does not mean that these children are going to recognize a three-dimensional cow from the picture nor will they understand that a puppy jumps. To them, the pictures or the words do not suggest action; they are static. The puppy is just there, in the air, not on his way up or down. The teacher must add the third dimension and the action.

If the children are allowed to hold the books as they like and to use whatever aids they like, they can learn and remember the two-dimensional visual symbols for word sounds. They can also comprehend what they have read, as long as the material touches their experience.

A child of this type has real difficulty in number concepts. Because of his reluctance to use his hands, he has not become very aware of his fingers as separate entities. If you have him lay his hands flat on a table, extended toward you on the opposite side with a piece of cardboard held so that he cannot see them, he is unlikely to be able to distinguish which finger you have touched. He has difficulty touching his thumb to each finger in succession. Research[24] suggests that there is some relation between this *finger agnosia* and the development of number concepts. The visual-somatic child's lack of experience in handling and manipulating objects may also be a contributing factor.

The aim of the pre-readiness work described was to create a willingness in this type of child to use his hands. Now, in the readiness period, the teacher can begin to help him toward further awareness. Finger plays, in which the teacher holds his hands and puts them through the action while reciting the little verses, are useful. The clay "snakes" can be "coiled" into little nests and little balls rolled for eggs; in some nests only one egg, in others two, three, or just "more than one." No rote counting should be allowed. Only number names which the child understands as useful should be encouraged. Everyday experiences, as in any kindergarten, can be used. Three children necessitate an equal number of chairs. The child can learn to say "one chair," "two chairs," "three chairs" as he brings them for use.

Motivating factors are extremely important for brain-injured children. For the visual-somatic child, teacher approval may be more potent than for the child in another category, but immediate concrete rewards are universally motivating, providing the reward is something the child really wants. Suppose favored pieces of candy are one cent each. After agreement on how many pieces a child is to buy, he can put a penny on each piece, counting as it is done. Then the candy and the pennies can be separated and each laid within a circle drawn on adjoining sheets of paper — for example, two matching groups of three. The main object in this readiness period is to help the visual-somatic child distinguish between one and more than one and to help him realize that every number name has a concrete meaning in terms of quantity — i.e. a group of objects which you can see and feel one by one.

Academic — Reading, Writing, Arithmetic

READING

In the preceding sections we have indicated that reading skills are not difficult for visual-somatic children. To quote the Epps, McCammon and Simmons[10] paraphrase of Gellner, "The reading difficulty for these children arises from a limited visual field and a disability of moving the eyes on visual stimulation. They must hold the words they read straight in front of their eyes. . . . These children will learn to read by any of the approved methods if the necessary allowances are made."

WRITING

There is quite a wide range among visual-somatic children as to the degree of involvement of the fine muscles used in writing. For some, writing is difficult to learn but finally mastered; for others it seems almost impossible. Forming the letters, keeping them in the correct sequence, and keeping them in some proximity to a line are all stumbling blocks. As usual, we must begin with touch and kinesthesis. The readiness work has prepared each child to use his fingers in a clay pan, to explore the shapes of letters in stencils and perhaps on sandpaper letters, and to hold and use a large crayon — thus, we are ready to put a large pencil in his hand to help him follow through the movements of making words, probably his own name to begin with.

For the children who find writing by hand almost insurmountable, there are bypasses. One is a stamping set of letters, though this is slow. Another is the use of a typewriter. Two instances come to mind in the author's experience in which fourth to fifth grade reading and spelling achievement were accompanied by writing so uneven and poorly formed as to be practically illegible. These children were highly frustrated by their inability to write acceptable letters. With a typewriter, once their reluctance to strike the keys was overcome by high motivation, their troubles were solved. They experienced for the first time the freedom to communicate by letter and the applause of the recipients of their efforts.

ARITHMETIC

In the small manual on teaching devices,[10] fifteen pages are devoted to handling numbers. This may reflect the difficulty of the subject, or only that more ingenious materials have been devised for it. As a general statement, one may say that concrete materials such as wooden cubes, beads and muffin tins for sorting, and abaci are used for every operation in the beginning. In this section, only one specific example will be given for the visual-somatic child. This is paraphrased from Epps.[10]

The teacher collected thread boxes, $5\frac{1}{2}$ x $2\frac{1}{2}$ inches, and painted them in plain colors to cover any printing. The numbers 1 through 5 were drawn in large quarter-inch-wide letters on labels.

One number was pasted on the top and inside the lid of each box. Small plastic cars, two inches long, were grouped in the boxes according to number and color. There was one blue car in a blue box, two yellow cars in a yellow box, and so on. Two procedures were used: (1) The child traced the number on top with his finger, opened the box, picked up and counted the cars aloud to his teacher, played with the cars, put them back and closed the lid. The color associations helped him to remember the number name and the number of objects associated with it. (2) The empty box was given to a child, and he had to select the right number of cars, from among others, to put into it. The colors assisted him. The objects in the box might be changed from time to time: two yellow cats or five black cats instead of yellow cars and black cars. This change may help to generalize the idea of the number. The teachers noted that the child's need for a device such as this lessens when his number concept exceeds five.

In summary, the visual-somatic child, at whatever general ability level, is likely to get along better with adults than with his peers because he is a non-participator in the active life of childhood. In order to learn a motor skill, he must be put through it passively at first. There is usually a wide gap between his reading and arithmetic achievement in favor of reading, but even his reading is limited in scope. If he has a high level of intelligence, he may succeed in sedentary and scholastic pursuits when he reaches adulthood. If he has less than normal intellectual ability, his training should be oriented toward fields of communication and social relations rather than manual skills.

Visual-Autonomic Children

Deficits and Strengths

These are the "hyperkinetic" children who explore their world through movement. They find little pleasure or meaning from passively looking at two-dimensional presentations such as pictures or books. They do enjoy flipping the pages. Colors are not as meaningful to them as the stronger contrasts of black and white, but the need to look at anything static long enough to remember it seems to weary them. Their levels of performance from day to day in the visual field seem to vary with inner and outer environmental states more than do those of children in the other categories. For example, differences in lighting, in physiological conditions, and the ordinary minor variations in emotional comfort seem to have a disproportionate effect upon their achievement levels. The difficulty they experience in learning to write is not in forming the letters, but in remembering the shapes to draw and in connecting names with the appropriate symbols. Though they can handle three-dimensional materials, their interest in action seems to produce a trial and error rather than a planned approach, and the end result in free constructive activity is unbalanced or bizarre. Form cues on puzzles are more useful than color or meaning, and these children can often construct a puzzle as well or better from the back as from the front.

A developmental history of a visual-autonomic child often shows no recognition of a problem in the early months. Motor and speech development were on schedule. Hyperactivity was usually the first difficulty when the baby attained locomotion and was "into everything." Later in preschool, kindergarten or first grade, when he was first asked to conform in a group, his troubles began with complaints from teachers that he disrupted the program. Failure to respond to the early visual-readiness materials and a subsequent reading disability followed.

This child's strengths lie in his good motor control, his responsiveness to movement and rhythm and his memory for phenomena related to these. An interesting item is his ability to find his way to a place he has once visited. Mothers say, "He can tell you every turn on the way home." If he has not experienced rejection, he is apt to be an outgoing, social child; if he has a pleasing personality, other children like him because of his activity skills. The very real handicaps of this child are perhaps least observable, as such, to casual acquaintances.

Principles for Remediation

PRE-READINESS LEVEL

This child does not need encouragement to use his hands. The important thing is not to discourage him from doing so, because this is his method of testing, learning, and interpreting the environment. In normal children, this seems to be largely taken over by the eyes in the first year of life. Quite young children understand that the doggie in the picture represents the doggie in the yard. With these children, a structured situation with an auditory link may be needed to help them bridge the gap between the three-dimensional object and the pictured representation. This is true of visual-somatic children also, but in the opposite direction. If they have rubber play animals which they can manipulate, they may learn to recognize the pictured *giraffe* by repeating the name while they explore the three-dimensional animal tactually.

Color recognition and naming may be strengthened by having a child sort different-shaped beads into muffin tins. All of one shape should be of the same color. Sorting by shape is not difficult for him, and the action keeps him interested. His attention should be called to the colors by verbal naming — " a *round yellow* bead here, a *square blue* bead here." Because of the quick visual fatigue experienced by these children, however, even three-dimensional tasks which require concentrated visual attention are to be used very sparingly. The general principle is to make looking at things pleasurable and rewarding, and this can be done only by the use of short tasks with materials which permit success upon almost a fleeting glance.

Gradually, with increasing maturity, experience, and motivation, the two-dimensional representations will convey meaning; or the child may learn to use the verbal bridge himself, and so fatigue will be delayed. An ingenious teacher may think of many ways to use movement, strong contrasts in black and white, and three-dimensional materials to catch and hold the child's pleased attention. One suggestion is to draw with phosphorescent pencil on a blackboard, as was done years ago by Guggenbuehl in 1860.

READINESS LEVEL

The contrast between teaching technique for the visual-autonomic and the visual-somatic is strongest at this level. For the visual-autonomic, we are striving to strengthen recognition and memory of two-dimensional symbols such as pictures, letters, and numbers, through the use of movement, manipulation, and three-dimensional associations; with the visual-somatic we are attempting to teach the three-dimensional meaning of the symbols which are easily recognized and remembered on a verbal level. For example, in the field of number concepts, the visual-autonomic child can count objects verbally and group them, but does not recognize the written symbol; the visual-somatic child can count by rote and recognize the symbol, but cannot count or group objects.

Readiness activities in counting and grouping with sticks, cubes, beads, little cars, or any similar materials can proceed in a conventional manner for an autonomic child as long as the response is verbal and color is not one of the cues. A child would be asked to count the *square* blocks, not count the *red* blocks. If there are five blocks, one of the ways to help him recognize, remember, and use the figure 5 for this group is to have him place the blocks on a sheet of paper on which the number 5 is dotted. He then connects the dots to form the solid letter.

Stenciled numbers made of tag board with slits just wide enough for the pencil point are also called "very specific for the visual-autonomic child who has difficulty writing numbers in the correct orientation." Or the child may stamp a number of line drawings of an object with a stamp set and be helped to select the correct number stamp to represent how many he stamped. Epps et al.,[10] highly recommend competitive games such as Pick-up-Sticks.℗ The child is good at these games and is likely to win, so learning to keep score is motivating. Other games recommended are Bean Bag,℗ Dart Ball,℗ and Ring Toss,℗ where the targets have score numbers on them. The authors say, "These games involve movement which gives great pleasure to the child with the visual-autonomic handicap. Since he enjoys playing these games, it motivates him to concentrate, and when he forces himself to look at the numbers, he is often able to recognize and remember them."

In general, the essence of the educational approach to the visual-autonomic child, for both number work and reading, is expressed in the above quote. The teacher must find materials and activities which give the child enough intrinsic pleasure to motivate him to pay high attention, even if momentary, to the symbols which he usually avoids.

Academic — Reading, Writing, Arithmetic

Preparation of the visual-autonomic child for reading must proceed along the same lines as outlined for arithmetic, but the complications of innumerable word forms make it much more difficult. The facts are that children with this handicap are likely always to be more advanced in arithmetic than in reading. Nevertheless, with good preparation in which they have learned to recognize and form the letters and attach a phonic value to them, they can proceed in reading with a careful phonic approach and much emphasis on writing. In building a vocabulary the steps should be (1) writing the word in strong black on white or white on black, (2) pronouncing the word for the child, (3) having him sound it out phonetically, (4) having him write it from his own phonetic dictation, and (5) repeating this process at frequent intervals until he recognizes it at sight. Equal care must be used that he knows the meaning. If the word is a noun that can be illustrated, use three-dimensional objects when possible. If it is a verb, let the child act it out when possible. Even abstract words, such as *anger, love,* and *happiness,* can be illustrated dramatically by puppets or plays which provide great fun with action and are extremely satisfying. When the child is far enough along, the use of record albums provides the auditory cue with the visual material. It is well for the children to do considerable reading aloud; to slow them down, provide kinesthetic experience of the word and assurance that they are getting the meaning — they will do quite well if they have read the words correctly.

In summary, the visual-autonomic child is likely to experience rejection from adults because his high activity level may be difficult to control. Nevertheless, this is his method of learning, and the effort should be to channel rather than to repress it. His quick visual fatigue and tendency to avoid static, two-dimensional visual stimuli can be overcome only by use of high motivation and brightness or movement in the stimuli. Perhaps because he has no deficit in awareness of his body-image, he has less difficulty in number concepts than the visual-somatic child but more handicap in learning to read both words and numbers.

Auditory-Somatic Children

Strengths and Weaknesses

These children may not use language at all, or they may have a late-developed, scanty vocabulary, usually with a speech defect. They may or may not understand language addressed to them at or above the level they use. Handicaps in the language field are particularly fraught with danger for these children, because failure to communicate verbally makes diagnosis difficult and frustration and misunderstanding very high. Particularly if one of these children is born into a highly verbal and intellectual family, his deficit makes him such a misfit that the emotional disturbance may be more obvious than the disability and the disturbance may be considered the cause of it. Suspicion of deafness, autism, aphasia, usually suggested and possibly ruled out after treatment, may subject the child to a series of experiences which only increase his confusion. The same child, born into a stable working-class family may fare much better. There may be less general conversation, less verbal ability expected, and the mother may find natural, gesticulative ways of communicating simple commands, so that a minimum of emotional conflict results, and the child makes the best use of the abilities he has. These may lie in any non-verbal activity — e.g., mechanical, artistic, or athletic. Even though his academic education may be in a special class, his other accomplishments should compensate for his lacks and fit sufficiently into his family pattern to win him praise and acceptance.

The difficult problem, in either setting, may be the child's own frustration in making his wants known. He may develop severe temper tantrums. These will be only more severe if some advisor tells the family, "He is slow in talking only because he does not have to. He has learned to get everything he wants without naming it." This puts the family on the spot and initiates a regime, probably inconsistent, of attempting to force language by deprivation. This is more likely to happen to the child who appears to understand language. The child who obviously does not understand may be mistaken for and treated as a deaf child, which is a better way of handling him even if not technically correct.

In reviewing the developmental history of these children, one finds that they may never have gone through the usual babbling play and sound imitation of infancy. They are late or unable in learning to differentiate articulated sounds and to attach meaning to them, though they may be oversensitive to noises. They may also enjoy music and be able to hum tunes. They may show no startle reaction to sound, and there may be other physical or neurological disturbances. The parents will likely describe the main problem as one of speech.

These children may be intact in visual perception. They have no difficulty with color or form perception, can handle three-dimensional tasks as well as two-dimensional, and can imitate form and movement in learning to write and to use their hands and bodies.

Principles for Remediation

PRE-READINESS LEVEL

The first step with auditory-somatic children is to reduce attempts at verbal communication to a minimum and to make the world a visual one. Speech should not be required of these children. The names of greatly desired objects such as *candy, ball, car,* can be clearly pronounced when the object is given, but no pressure should be brought to have a child repeat this sound. The teacher may use vivid lipstick and encourage the child to watch the movements of her lips, i.e., to use visual speech as in lip reading. In time the child may come to associate a simple word symbol with the object and still later may try to use a sound for it himself, which may not be a very good reproduction. He may be said to have a *speech defect.* No pressure should be brought to correct him, or he may give up trying. Only the word should be correctly repeated after him in a pleased tone as the object is forthcoming so that he is rewarded for his effort.

As he begins to build up a small, concrete vocabulary, short phrases with the illustrated movement and gesture may be used, such as *come here, sit down.* Words should never be used to scold or punish the child. His associations with them must always be pleasant and rewarding, and the initiative in using them must be left to him. Words can be used in songs as part of the music, but the child should not be asked to learn these words or to get meaning from them without visual cues.

READINESS LEVEL

Because so much of the academic readiness material in kindergarten work relies on visual-motor abilities, these children have little difficulty. They can color within lines, cut, paste and match forms, and perform all the readiness activities so long as no recitation is involved. They learn to match and recognize word forms and connect them with appropriate pictures and actions, and to draw lines from the number forms to the appropriate groups if no verbal naming is involved.

Academic — Reading, Writing, Arithmetic

There is an almost unlimited supply of materials which can be used in a visual approach toward teaching these children to read silently for meaning: picture-word lotto games; picture-word matching cards, which can be combined into stories; picture dictionaries; and pictured action. For example, silhouette word-action cards are displayed. These are pictures of a child doing something such as running, jumping, hopping, or skipping. The word is printed on a strip below the picture. The auditory-somatic child is shown how and encouraged to repeat the action. Later he is shown only the word as a cue for his action. The teacher may say the word, but no verbal response is required from the child. At a later stage he may put words together to form a short sentence and show the meaning by action. As he advances, since he will be having no more than ordinary difficulty in writing, he can begin to indicate his grasp of the material he reads by responding in writing. For example, the sentence "Tom threw the ————." could be completed when the child selects the correct choice from a series showing a picture of each object and its name, e.g., "picture of a ball" — *ball*, "picture of a bat" — *bat*, "picture of a bell" — *bell*.

A dramatic example of the responses of a child with a relatively mild auditory-somatic difficulty was observed in one of our research studies.[13] The boy was able to carry on conversation about simple, concrete experiences, and he was working at a fourth-grade level in reading and spelling. The research task required the child first to arrange a series of pictures in proper sequences to tell stories, and second to give back verbally in sequence a series of events in short recorded stories. This child ranked first in the group in the picture sequences, and in the auditory sequences he ranked near the bottom; he became so frustrated that he burst into tears and began to abuse the record player verbally.

In summary, these children with an auditory-somatic handicap are in danger of developing severe emotional maladjustment because of misunderstanding and frustration. They must be taught through visual materials and devices. Since much teaching material relies on vision, it is relatively easy to devise ways of avoiding the need for verbal response. It is to be hoped that, as his intellect develops, this child will progress in speech also, but this must not be pushed, only encouraged. Not until the child is using language with relative freedom should any formal correction of speech defects be undertaken.

Auditory-Autonomic Children

Deficits and Strengths

These children can reproduce verbal patterns with as much facility as the visual-autonomic children can copy action, but the words are just sound patterns to them, not symbols to convey meaning. When a child of this type is trying to volunteer information, he has great difficulty finding a word to use; he does not understand the meaning of what is said to him, so that he may not respond appropriately when asked a direct question. This is one of his great dangers, because he may often be blamed and punished for disobedience, stubbornness, or lying when he does not perform as instructed. It is difficult to believe that anyone so verbal, who may repeat long stretches of conversations he has heard, does not understand simple instructions. If he has met with too much censure, he may stop talking when others are around and withdraw from painful human contacts. Whereas, the auditory-somatic child may be diagnosed as autistic, an auditory-autonomic child is frequently seen as a childhood schizophrenic because he seems to have regressed after having been verbal and outgoing at one time.

The developmental histories of these children often show that for the first year or two their parents considered them normal or precocious. Their motor development proceeded on schedule, they began early to use word patterns, and often could repeat whole nursery rhymes and imitate long words. Only as the parents began to notice that their child did not actually answer questions asked him, or that he responded only by repetition of the question, did they begin to feel there was something odd or different about him.

On the other hand, this child has all the positive abilities described for the auditory-somatic child, i.e. good visual perception and motor control and, in addition, he *can* imitate word patterns. The task, in this case, is to help him associate these words with the meanings which his eyes and muscles give him.

Principles for Remediation

PRE-READINESS LEVEL

The talkativeness of the auditory-autonomic child may become tiresome. Nevertheless, he should not be too discouraged from talking while positive efforts are made to help him associate meaning with his words. It is difficult to realize that he does not understand, because he often produces words in the proper context. For example, with an older child, the sight of an orange may cause him to say *orange*. He has heard this word often in association with this visual object. When no orange is present, and he is asked, "What is an orange?" he can come up with no attribute, such as shape, color, or use. Neither can he tell you what it is he wants should he want an orange, except, perhaps, by an awkward type of circumlocution or a gesture.

As the visually handicapped child must be given an auditory link, a child with a language handicap must be given a visual and kinesthetic link between the sound of the word and the meaningful associations. As with the somatic category, language should be used with him only when it is associated with other meaningful experiences. Small rubber animals or pictured and real household articles can be given to him and the name pronounced as he handles them. Terms such as *big, little, long,* or *short* should all be demonstrated along with the word. This is more or less standard practice in all nursery schools. With a child of this type, especial care must be used to see that he really gets the meaning.

READINESS LEVEL

As with the auditory-somatic child, most of the usual readiness materials can be used with the auditory-autonomic child. The ever-present caution is to be sure that every word *said* to him is given visual meaning through illustration or gesture, and that the child be helped to understand that language is a means of communication not just a pleasing auditory-motor activity to be reproduced, like a tune.

Academic — Reading, Writing, Arithmetic

If an English-speaking person has learned to pronounce German words and to associate them phonetically with certain printed symbols, he can read flawlessly without getting a single idea from the whole performance. Auditory-autonomic children can do this with their mother tongue. They can also write and spell since they have good memories in these fields. Rote arithmetic, as with the visual-somatic children, is not too difficult, but real functional arithmetic may have little relation to the verbalized activity.

To quote from Epps,[10] "The child with an auditory-autonomic handicap, though able to hear, repeat, and remember the number name, is often unable to remember the exact meaning of the number name. He can only connect a word with its significance if its sound calls forth immediately the mental image of a visual or tactile object. . . ." In short, he remembers words but is uncertain with which visual symbol or group of objects it should be connected. Concrete devices of all kinds should be used in helping a child of this type to master the basic facts of arithmetic. At the same time, he should be encouraged to verbalize his work and to write it so that connections will be formed between the words, the facts, and the visual symbols.

An excellent example of these difficulties was observed in the case of a boy whose measured retardation was mild but, being ataxic and blocked also in other avenues of approach, he was never able to achieve academically. He was quite able to count by rote to one hundred or over. He could also say the alphabet. He enjoyed playing Dominoes since he recognized the matching groups, and he could put the correct number of objects, such as five beads, into the box with the 5 on it. He was not sure what to call it. If asked to count and tally, he usually skipped verbally or repeated so that he did not come out right. If asked to find a date on the calendar, he usually began counting at one and continued carefully aloud until he reached the required word sound, with his finger on the visual symbol. In spite of a severe speech defect, he was an avid talker; the vocabulary he used was wide, but he did not listen to the meaning expressed by others. He never was able to name a printed word out of its context (he quickly memorized a printed word if it was read to him). It was not that he did not recognize the word visually, only that the meaningful sound pattern was not firmly connected with it, and he called it anything which seemed likely. This child's disability was especially severe because there was also a slight visual-autonomic dysfunction. Nevertheless, he grew up with a quite stable and pleasant personality, and he is now doing well working in the institution greenhouse.

In the uncomplicated case, one relies constantly on visual cues to give meaning. Use of a picture dictionary should be strongly encouraged. Picture-word matching cards and record albums are examples of providing a specific visual cue. Combining silent reading with writing is especially meaningful for an auditory-autonomic child as a means for achievement. Seeing a picture of the object and the word and hearing the word simultaneously are reinforced by writing the word. Later a test can be given by showing the pictures and asking the child to write the word. Another good device is the See Quees,℗ or sequence puzzles, in which a story is told in successive pictures. This type of child can get the meaning from the pictures, and an accompanying text should be presented using the simplest words possible. The text should be read to the child. Later he can be given the pictures alone and be encouraged to tell, or to write and tell the story. In choosing the child's readers, care should be taken that the pictures follow the text closely so that visual cues to meaning are clear.

In short, one must be sure that the child understands the meaning of every word used in his instruction; the way to do this is through visual cues. Learning to write should be no special problem for these children. Writing can be used as a device for reinforcing the verbal forms which accompany the visual presentation. Dramatized stories are excellent for helping the child gain meaning from words.

In summary, the auditory-autonomic child, like his counterpart in the visual field, has trouble in perception of meaning of the symbolic stimuli which he hears but he can imitate them. He should not be blamed or scolded for his perseverative or inappropriate verbal activity, but should be helped, through vision and kinesthesis, to associate meaning with word patterns to control his own verbal expressions. Repression and rejection often result in withdrawal, and the emotional maladjustment may seem to overshadow the perceptual deficit. Early diagnosis and patient training of these children are essential.

Group Activities for All

Music and Record Readers

Most children in any group will find something to enjoy in a well-managed music period, although each will enjoy it in his own way. There may be a few auditory-somatic children who find only discomfort in these occasions, and they should never be compelled to join the group. Pictures illustrating the songs must always be provided. Freedom to act out the music appropriately should be allowed. Thus, the visual-somatic child may sit and enjoy the singing; the visual-autonomic child may beat sticks or caper to the rhythms; the auditory-somatic child may hum the tunes and look at the pictures; and the auditory-autonomic may sing along and be helped to use pictures and actions as cues to the word meanings. There should never be tension or a feeling of *must,* only enjoyment and relaxation. Because of this pleasant atmosphere, music period may be highly effective for teaching meanings in each type of deficit and for encouraging an attitude of tolerance and belongingness in the group. Each child should have his turn to choose his favorite music.

Group Games

Not many brain-injured children in any beginning group show much social feeling toward peers. Sociability may never develop to a high degree, but it can be encouraged and improved to some degree. Following are suggestions of the types of group activities which may start the younger children on the road to social acceptance. This is also an illustration of the fact that the child's deficit must be taken into consideration in all areas of his activities — not just in his academic learning.

Visual-Somatic Children

1. Marching or circle type games which do not demand skill — such as "The King of France," "London Bridge," "Farmer in the Dell."
2. Table games: Picture Lotto℗, Picture Dominoes℗, "Old Maid."℗ or similar card games — all of which require simple matching and recognition.
3. Activities shared with a group. Interaction encouraged but not necessary.
   (a) Listening to story records and joining in at appropriate occasions.
   (b) Group singing with some simple structured dramatic accompaniment such as "This Old Man," which can be repeated in the same form. The child can be put through the movement, if necessary, until the movements are learned.
   (c) Simple cooking, such as cutting out cookies with a cookie cutter and baking them.

4. Dramatic activities. A wide variety of short stories, poems or songs may be used in which a character is assigned to a child. Action is not necessary. For example, "The Three Little Pigs" requires four characters who speak almost the same lines. The rest may be read by the narrator.

VISUAL-AUTONOMIC CHILDREN

1. Active group games such as "In and Out the Window," "Did You Ever See a Lassie?" "This is the Way We Wash our Clothes," "Follow the Leader," "Make a Motion."
2. Games which are fast moving: Cootie℗, jacks, Ring Toss℗, Tenpins℗, table tennis, spinner games.
3. Activities shared with a group.
   (a) Listening to story records with pictured accompaniment.
   (b) Acting out story records.
   (c) Visits to institution facilities such as the bakery, and representation of some of these activities in the classroom.
4. Dramatic activities. These may be somewhat formal in the sense of acting out short stories or using puppets or may be completely informal in the sense of providing materials for spontaneous dramatic play. Dress-up clothes, housekeeping adjuncts, cowboy and Indian props, blocks and small cars may all be used by these children to rapid moving play, which encourages social interaction. The important aspect in guiding these activities for social development is that the children be carefully grouped so that competition is fair and each child can feel adequate.

AUDITORY-SOMATIC AND AUDITORY-AUTONOMIC CHILDREN

These children need activities in which verbal instructions are not given.

1. Circle or activity games which can be easily demonstrated such as Drop the Handkerchief, Follow the Leader, Statues.
2. Table or floor games. These children like games of skill,

such as jacks, marbles, jackstraws, simple card games, which involve mainly visual matching, Picture Lotto℗.

3. Activities shared with a group such as working together on a poster or decorative strip, setting up class projects — farm, store, etc., group singing with illustrative movement.

4. Dramatic activities. Most typical for this group would be pantomime.

DISCUSSION

It is difficult to assess the results of any specific teaching method because of the number of variables involved. No two groups of children are really similar no matter how carefully paired on objective measures such as Binet IQs, MAs, achievement tests, or socioeconomic backgrounds, to mention only a few of the various items to be found in the literature. There are always the unknown variables such as teachers' personalities, parental responses, differences in the physical environment, to say nothing of the differences in the children themselves and sometimes in testers.

Matching groups of children with special learning deficits becomes next to impossible, since no two children have exactly the same problem. The most valid test would be to take a group of children whose achievement levels and rates of progress have been measured over a period of time with a good teacher; educate this teacher in a specific method; and measure the progress made by the same children with the same teacher, using the new method. This, too, has its flaws because of the increasing maturity level of the children, other intangibles, and numerous practical barriers.

Such comparative experiments as have been undertaken in teaching brain-injured children by special methods have had rather discouraging results. In the opinions of people who use Gellner techniques, any experiment which uses only the "exogenous-endogenous" or "brain-injured — non-brain-injured" types of matching is doomed to poor results, because the children are neither matched nor taught in relation to specific deficits, and their real differences cancel each other out in the averages. Research in Project Number 50, therefore, has been directed more toward demonstrating the differences in response to various perceptual and learning situations between the visual-perceptual handicaps one the one hand and the auditory-perceptual handicaps on the other.[7,13,14,15,16]

Just completed in June of 1966 was a comparative teaching experiment. The children were carefully paired for deficits on the Gellner tests and for CA, MA, and IQ on the Binet. One group was taught for eighteen months by an excellent teacher with no Gellner knowledge or background, and the other group was taught by a teacher experienced over several years in Gellner techniques. Then the groups were exchanged for another eighteen months. The results of this experiment are now being assessed.

It was mentioned earlier that the neat categories we have described are seldom encountered singly, especially in an institution population. If a child is so severely damaged as to be institutionalized at an early age, it is unlikely that his deficit is in one area only. Usually one handicap is more severe and obvious. The child tends to be hyperactive or awkward, or mute or chattery, but a milder degree of other deficits is usually present. If he has a severe visual-autonomic defect, for example, so that he gets little meaning from pictures or printed matter, and we are attempting to use an auditory approach, success is limited if he has also an auditory deficit, either somatic or autonomic, even if mild. The most dramatic successes described to us have been with children of average or superior general ability in the public schools who suffered from a circumscribed specific disability. These children are best able to make use of a new approach offered them.

Dr. Gellner believed, when she was with us, that children who had been diagnosed as moderately retarded (IQ 35-50) could be returned to society as normal individuals if a path to the intact cortex around the block in the midbrain could be reached early enough. Of this we have yet to be convinced. We have returned a number of our children to the community greatly improved both socially and achievement wise, but IQs in the forties were not prepared for independent competitive existence. This may only prove that we have not translated Dr. Gellner's principles into specific teaching methods with sufficient insight into the needs of the child. (Dr. Gellner has just returned to England after two years of a new experiment in the Special Education Department of the Public Schools of Colorado Springs, Colorado. This was reported in a panel of the ninetieth meeting of the AAMD in May of 1966 at Chicago. No publications have, as yet, come to our attention.)

Another problem exists in the diagnostic field. Severe emotional maladjustment may depress a child's functional level. When the regressed behavior begins with the misunderstanding of a disability, help with the disability may result in improved emotional stability and responsiveness, and the child who appeared severely retarded may be given a brighter prognosis to a dramatic degree. Such cases, though rare in institutional experience, do occur, sometimes regardless of the specific program used, and are welcomed as if miraculous; but if the reason for the improvement is not known, they are not instructive and are actually discouraging to effort. The events which are heartening to teachers and investigators are the observable results from the application of carefully devised methods which can be duplicated. By this test, the Gellner concepts appear to stand up well as stimuli to teaching interest and research hypotheses.

REFERENCES

1. Bensberg, G. J.: The relationship of the academic achievement of mental defectives to mental age, sex, institutionalization and etiology. *Amer J Ment Defic, 58:*327-30, 1953.
2. Bensberg, G. J., and Cantor, G. N.: Reaction time in mental defectives with organic and familial etiology. *Amer J Ment Defic, 62:*534-7, 1957.
3. Birch, H. G.: Summary of Conference. Symposium on Research Design and Methodology in Mental Retardation. AAMD — Woods School Conference, May 1959. *Amer J Ment Defic, 64:*413, 1959.
4. Bradley, Betty Hunt: Differential responses in perceptual ability among mentally retarded brain-injured children. *J Educ Res, 57:*421-4, 1964.
5. Bradley, Betty Hunt; Maurer, Ruth, and Hundziak, Marcel: A study of the effectiveness of milieu therapy and language training for the mentally retarded. *Exceptional Child,* Nov. 1966, pp. 143-50.
6. Capobianco, R. J.: Quantitative and qualitative analyses of endogenous and exogenous boys on arithmetic achievement. *Monogr Soc Res Child Develop, 19:*58, 101-42, 1954.
7. Clevenger, L. J.: The effectiveness of learning in mentally retarded brain-

injured children when taught by methods specific to their handicaps. Unpublished Master's Thesis, Ohio State University, 1960.

8. Cromwell, R. L., and Foshee, J. G.: Studies in activity level. IV. Effects of visual stimulation during task performance in mental defectives. *Amer J Ment Defic, 65:*248-51, 1960.

9. Cruickshank, W. M.; Bentzen, Frances; Ratzburg, F. H., and Tannhauser, Mirian T.: *A Teaching Method for Brain-injured and Hyperactive Children.* New York, Syracuse, 1961.

10. Epps, Helen O.; McCammon, Gertrude B., and Simmons, Queen D.: *Teaching Devices for Children with Impaired Learning.* Columbus, Parent Volunteer Association of the Columbus State School, Inc., 1958.

11. Gallagher, J. J.: *The Tutoring of Brain-injured Mentally Retarded Children. Springfield,* Thomas, 1960.

12. Gellner, Lise: *A Neurophysiological Concept of Mental Retardation and its Educational Implications.* Chicago, Levinson Research Foundation, 1959.

13. Hunt, Betty, and Patterson, Ruth M.: Performance of brain-injured and familial mentally deficient children on visual and auditory sequences. *Amer J Ment Defic, 63:*72-80, 1958.

14. Hunt, Betty M.: Performance of mentally deficient brain-injured and mentally deficient familial children on construction from patterns. *Amer J Ment Defic, 63:*679-87, 1959.

15. Hunt, Betty M.: Differential responses of mentally deficient brain-injured children and mentally deficient familial children to meaningful auditory material. *Amer J Ment Defic, 64:*747-53, 1960.

16. Hunt, Betty M.: Differential responses of mentally retarded children on the Leiter Scale. *Exceptional Child, 28:*99-102, 1961.

17. Kephart, N. C.: *The Slow Learner in the Classroom.* Columbus, Merrill, C. E., 1960.

18. Kirk, S. A., and McCarthy, J. J.: The Illinois Test of Psycholinguistic Abilities — an approach to differential diagnosis. *Amer J Ment Defic, 66:*399-412, 1961.

19. Kirk, S. A.: *Educating Exceptional Children.* Boston, Houghton, 1962.

20. Pasamanick, B.: Research on the influence of sociocultural variables upon organic factors in mental retardation. *Amer J Ment Defic, 64:*316-22, 1959.

21. Sloan, W., and Bensberg, G. J.: The stereognostic capacity of brain-injured as compared with familial mental defectives. *J Clin Psychol, 7:*154-6, 1951.

22. Strauss, A. A., and Kephart, N. C.: *Psychopathology and education of the brain-injured child. Vol. 2, Progress in Theory and Clinic.* New York, Grune, 1955.

23. Strauss, A. A., and Lehtinen, Laura E.: *Psychopathology and Education of the Brain-injured Child.* New York, Grune, 1947.
24. Strauss, A. A., and Werner, H.: Deficiency in the finger schema in relation to arithmetic disability. *Amer J Orthopsychiat, 8:*719-24, 1938.

IX

A TREATMENT PROGRAM FOR CHILDREN WITH LEARNING DIFFICULTIES

MARIANNE FROSTIG

THIS CHAPTER IS BASED upon direct experiences and research with children with learning difficulties in the Marianne Frostig Center of Educational Therapy (hereafter referred to as the Center) and in public schools. Over two hundred children are enrolled at the Center at any given time. Over three hundred children are evaluated psychologically, psychiatrically, and educationally in a given year. The Center combines educational facilities with the services of a child guidance clinic. In addition to the treatment facilities and diagnostic services provided for the children and their families, the Center also undertakes research and teacher-training.

DIAGNOSTIC CATEGORIES

Children are referred to the Center subsequent to failure in public school. Their common characteristics are difficulty in learning and poor school adjustment, but their specific problems vary. Their medical and psychiatric diagnostic classifications also vary. Examples of the initial diagnoses include chronic brain syndrome of unknown or unspecified cause, chronic brain syndrome with neurotic reaction, adjustment reaction of childhood, or simply learning disturbance.

In a diagnostic survey of a sample of one hundred seventeen children enrolled at the Center since January of 1965, the children were grouped under three major classifications. The first category was composed of fifty-four children with learning difficulties in whom organic etiology apparently played a decisive role. The diagnoses subsumed under this category included *chronic brain syndrome, chronic brain dysfunction with neurotic or psychotic reaction, mental deficiency with possible cerebral dysfunction,* and *learning disturbances with minimal cerebral dysfunction.*

The second category was composed of thirty-four children in whom emotional disturbances were thought to be causative. This category subsumed diagnoses which included *learning disturbance with neurosis, adjustment reaction of childhood,* and *adjustment reaction of adolescence.* The third category was composed of twenty-nine children who were given the diagnostic label of *learning disturbance.**

In addition to this attempt at etiological diagnosis, an evaluation of the underlying disabilities was undertaken. An assessment was carried out in the areas of visual and auditory perception, language, and higher thought processes. In this sample, many children were found to show multiple developmental deficits *whatever* the etiological diagnosis. There was a relative lack of correspondence between medical diagnosis and developmental status. However, the evidence of this survey suggested that children with known or suspected organic disturbance showed severe disturbances in perceptual functions more frequently than those children classified as emotionally disturbed.

It was concluded that medical diagnosis has implications for such aspects of the child's management as psychotherapy, parent counseling, additional medical help and the possible use of medication, and referral to inpatient facilities; however, it has no bearing on the design of the child's curriculum or on decisions with regard to classroom grouping and management. The management of the child in school relates primarily to the results of the evaluation of the underlying processes which cause the learning difficulties.

PSYCHOLOGICAL EVALUATION

The most effective remedial program is probably one which is based upon detailed and comprehensive testing and observation. The school psychologist and the educational therapist can then translate the results of the testing and observation into a program of training specifically designed to help the child develop the basic psychological functions found to be deficient. A careful choice of testing instruments is therefore important.

---

*All diagnoses listed are according to current APA terminology.

There are two widely used tests specifically designed to serve as a partial basis for remedial programs. Samuel Kirk and his associates at the University of Illinois, concerned with the need for an educationally oriented measure with which to evaluate specific language disturbances, developed the Illinois Test of Psycholinguistic Abilities[9] (see Appendix II for suggested instructional procedures related to test measures). The staff of the Frostig Center, out of a related concern, developed the Frostig Developmental Test of Visual Perception[2,12] (see Appendix III for suggested instructional procedures related to test measures). These two tests have become integral to the evaluation of all children at the Center. In addition to the ITPA and the Frostig, the Wepman Test of Auditory Discrimination[14] and the Wechsler Intelligence Scale for Children are used with children in the elementary grades for the assessment of auditory perception and higher cognitive functions respectively. The total test battery often includes additional tests depending upon the needs of the child. The entire evaluation program — testing, interviewing, and observing — is designed to assess each child's specific strengths and weaknesses in six areas: sensory-motor functions, language, perception, higher cognitive processes, and social and emotional development.

The results of the four basic tests (the ITPA, Frostig, Wepman and WISC) are entered by the teacher on the *Basic Test Results* sheet (see Appendix IV). The results of the child's achievement tests are noted on the same sheet. This sheet forms a useful graphic guide for the teacher and, in general, serves to highlight areas which require attention.

In a sample of seventy-eight children taken from the Center, it was possible to document (See Appendix I) the results of the Wepman, the Frostig, and the ITPA. It was found that no less than two-thirds of these children scored in the lowest quartile of the Frostig Test; over 43 per cent evidenced difficulties on the Wepman Test; and almost 54 per cent had a total language age on the ITPA which was at least .30 below the mean standard score. Many of the children at the Center showed perceptual difficulties in both the visual and the auditory modality. Visual and auditory perceptual functions, as measured by the Frostig and the Wepman, were disturbed in 41 per cent of the population. Analysis of the subtests of the ITPA revealed that visual-motor sequencing difficulties were most frequent. In general, the children at the Center exhibited characteristics similar to those of samples described by Kass[8] and by Graubard.[7] Kass, who explored the psycholinguistic abilities of children with reading problems, reported that the majority of children in her sample had difficulties in four subtests: auditory-verbal sequencing, which taps memory for numbers; auditory-vocal automatic, which tests grammatical speech; visual-motor sequencing, which taps the ability to remember the order of a series of figures or pictures; and auditory-vocal association, which requires the completion of analogies. Graubard, who studied delinquent children who were non-readers, found the greatest deficits at the integrational level in the visual-motor channel and in grammatical speech.

What are the implications of such findings for the child's education? It is clear that perceptual abilities, auditory and visual memory, and automatic learning are frequently deficient in children with learning difficulties. Moreover, their memory defects may be highly specific, e.g., for numbers or for various kinds of visual patterns. Superimposed on such cognitive disabilities may be behavior disorders which interfere with learning.

All of these factors suggest that for most children with learning difficulties, a global approach to remedial education is necessary for best results. Visual-perceptual, sensory-motor, and language training (including auditory-perceptual training) seem to be most effective when used in combination, even though the emphasis may be on one or another aspect. Moreover, this approach is suggested regardless of the medical diagnosis and whether or not it specifies neurological involvement. It follows that since the characteristics of children with learning handicaps are so varied, remedial approaches must also be varied and made to correspond to the specific needs of each child.

We may define a need as the discrepancy between a child's actual level of performance in any area and the optimum level we believe he is capable of. Such discrepancies are implied in

children with learning difficulties who show a great degree of in-
tratest as well as intertest scatter. Children exhibiting such high
and low points in basic psychological functions are themselves
often aware of what Gallagher[6] has called their *developmental
imbalance*. The awareness of their disabilities tends to be emotionally upsetting. These emotional difficulties also need to be
taken into account in their educational plan.

The relative merits of three different approaches to training in
the basic abilities of sensory-motor functioning, perception, and
language and concept formation have been studied at the Center.
One approach consists of the use of separate training programs for
each of these major functions. The second approach uses one
program as the central emphasis, integrating training in the other
abilities with it. The third approach involves the integration of
ability training into the regular academic curriculum. Present
findings suggest that these three approaches need not be conceived of as alternatives, but rather as supplementary techniques
to be used in any appropriate combination. Emphasis is given in
the remainder of this chapter to the second approach. Since so
many of the Center's younger children evidence perceptual problems, the visual-perceptual program is used most frequently as the
core program with which training in other abilities is integrated.
For older children with similar difficulties, the regular curriculum
is more often used as the vehicle for ability training.

VISUAL-PERCEPTUAL TRAINING

The Frostig Program[3] consists of over three hundred and fifty
two-dimensional worksheet exercises and a Teacher's Guide which
contains suggestions for exercises in sensory-motor training and
in visual-perceptual training using three-dimensional objects.
This program discusses the importance of integrating language
training with the use of the workbooks. Suggestions for language
activities are included in later Teacher's Guides.[4,5] All of the
materials described, when integrated, constitute a portion of a
developmental readiness or remedial program for visual perception.

The Frostig Program is divided into five sections which correspond to the five perceptual functions evaluated by the test. The first set of worksheets trains visual-motor coordination. Motor-handicapped children may have to trace with their fingers before using a crayon or pencil. Tasks include drawing (straight, curved and angular lines between guide lines) , tracing, drawing lines to a target, coloring, and pre-writing exercises. The child who experiences difficulties with these tasks may be suffering from poor eye-muscle control, fine hand-muscle control, or poor eye-hand coordination.

The second group of worksheets is designed to improve figure-ground discrimination. The tasks include finding hidden figures, tracing intersecting figures, recognizing overlapping figures, finding similar or different details in drawings, and recognizing reversals of figure and ground. The third group of worksheets trains constancy of form and size perception. These sheets develop the ability to recognize simple geometrical figures regardless of the angle at which they are presented, to recognize pictures presented in various degrees of schematization, and to discriminate size. The fourth group of worksheets develops perception of position in space. These sheets train the ability to see the direction of a figure (whether it is turned right, left, up, or down) and to find rotations and reversals. There are also exercises in the recognition and drawing of identical and mirror-image patterns. The fifth group of worksheets trains the perception of spatial relationships. It includes copying patterns, the synthesis of mutilated figures, figure completion, and recognition of the direction of details within a whole.

Training in visual-perceptual skills should be geared to the test results. Perceptual areas in which children experience the greatest difficulties should receive the greatest emphasis. Whereas one child may require an emphasis on figure-ground perception, another may benefit most from training in eye-motor coordination, and still another in perception of position in space. Despite these separate emphases, all children should gain experience in every area. The time devoted to training in visual perception at the Center has averaged about one and one-half hours weekly. This time may be distributed into several schedules including daily sessions, or sessions occurring two or three times weekly. The number of sheets used will vary according to age level and difficulty of tasks. As many as eight to ten sheets may be used in a week. More time is necessary when various other developmental skills are systematically integrated with the program, or when the program is used with children with severe learning difficulties.

Additional training is provided by *Teacher's Guide to Beginning Pictures and Patterns*[4] which is designed to be used primarily for preventive and readiness purposes in regular nursery school, kindergarten, and primary grade classes. In this version, training exercises from the five areas of perceptual training are not presented in separate units, but are combined in a sequence in workbook form believed to facilitate easy and efficient lesson planning.

The various perceptual exercises described above, although geared to younger children, may be used with some benefit with older children with perceptual defects. Older children with lags in visual-perceptual development will usually need a longer period of training than younger children, and will need to have this material interspersed with age-related tasks with known interest value.

Initial testing, of course, greatly facilitates the most efficient use of remedial programs. If formal testing of visual perception, however, cannot be undertaken, the worksheets can serve the dual function of testing and training. The phrase *diagnostic use of therapy* applies here to the double use of the worksheets. While administering these worksheets, the teacher must observe the child's area of failure carefully so that appropriate additional training can be provided.

Most of the exercises described above train perception in two-dimensional space only. The training of perception in regard to a plane surface is of obvious importance for academic work; it should be offered both before and during the introduction of beginning academic skills. Children who perceive incorrectly what is presented on a two-dimensional surface have difficulty with the reproduction of written symbols (letters or numbers) and with all other paper and pencil or chalkboard work. But two-dimensional training alone is insufficient. It should be preceded and accompanied by activities with three-dimensional materials and by other forms of sensory-motor training. Visual-perceptual training with two-dimensional materials need not be postponed until the child has mastered the manipulative materials. Training with both kinds of activities can proceed simultaneously, augmenting and enhancing each other.

Training in language and concept formation is also necessary. Our clinical observations of the multiplicity of disturbances found in children with learning difficulties have been reinforced by reports from teachers in public school classrooms. The most satisfactory results with the exercises discussed have been reported from schools which reinforced the visual-perceptual training program with other kinds of training, including language and sensory-motor skills. Their findings emphasize the importance of integrating visual-perceptual training with training in language, sensory-motor functions, and concept formation.

SENSORY-MOTOR TRAINING

Training in the development of sensory-motor functions is attempted in four different areas: (1) general training of movement skills (through a program of physical education) ; (2) development of body awareness (an aspect of physical education which needs special emphasis) , (3) training in eye-hand coordination (through play with construction toys and various manipulative activities) , and (4) training in eye movement (through tracking exercises) .

The physical education program is based, in part, on various factor-analytic studies of movement.[13] The following attributes of movement are considered: gross body coordination, balance, flexibility, speed and agility, strength, and endurance. The development of body awareness is of utmost importance. The relationship between various forms of psychopathology and poor body-image is well-known. Children with learning difficulties often display poor awareness of their bodies. Such children often feel clumsy and incapable of important developmental activities involving motor ability. They are undoubtedly helped emotionally when they are aided in the development of their body awareness through motor activity.

Body awareness affects not only a person's self-image but also his perception of direction. Perceptually, a person may be said to be at the center of his own world. It is not surprising, therefore, that a child first learns direction in relation to his own body. For example, he must learn to perceive an object as being in front of himself before he can learn to perceive objects as being in front of each other. Similarly, he must learn where his own left hand or right hand is before he can learn which is the left and which the right hand of another person. If a child does not acquire the ability to lateralize and to accurately perceive the position and direction of objects, he is likely to have difficulty in learning to read and to write.[1,7]

The third section of the sensory-motor training program consists of training in eye-hand coordination through the encouragement of manipulative skills. This includes work with Montessorian materials, play with construction toys, model making, building with blocks, making patterns, cutting, origami folding, and various self-help activities. The fourth section, concerned with eye movement, emphasizes tracking exercises for dealing with erratic movements.

LANGUAGE TRAINING

Language, like visual perception, is not a unitary function. Language training, therefore, needs to take various forms. The language program at the Center contains sections which correspond to the subtests of the ITPA (see Appendix II). For purposes of language training, the attempt is made to conceptualize four broad areas of language: receptive language, expressive language, associative functions, and memory for verbal expression and semantic content. Training in receptive language is necessarily an integral part of the perceptual program since listening skills are needed whenever the teacher talks to the class, gives directions, imparts information, or asks questions. Training in all four areas should be integrated with the perceptual program and with the teaching of sensory-motor skills.

Much attention is paid to the encouragement of expressive language to compensate the difficulties engendered when schools emphasize listening to the neglect of expressive language. The integration of the use of expressive language with sensory-motor training is highly desirable and can be achieved by discussing and planning activities beforehand, by asking for suggestions for elaboration during the activity, and by stimulating evaluation and review after the activity. Similarly, verbal expression can be emphasized during perceptual exercises by having the children participate in planning and discussing the exercises.

The teacher can encourage development in the ability to deal with spatial and temporal references (in between, here, there, over, under, above, tomorrow, presently, last year) and words denoting relationships (farther, darker, but, although). The expressive function of writing needs also to be emphasized, and preparatory pre-writing exercises should be offered early with the expectation of leading quickly into written expression.

Illustration with gesture and movement as part of a language program can promote expression through movement and become integrated with the sensory-motor and perceptual program. Examples of activities include having the children demonstrate such things as how a bird flies, a tree bends in the wind, a person walks with a heavy load, a man saws wood, a child walks proudly home to show a good report card.

Associative functions are developed when the teacher helps the children to associate subject matter with later ideas discussed in class. To this end, what she teaches should be presented in an integrated form, e.g., in teaching *units*. It is desirable both to cut across subject matter within a given unit and to refer the content of one unit to another. Many teachers do not present subject matter in an integrated form. The child may learn on one occasion about *the rain* and other aspects of the climate and on another occasion about *flowers and plants,* without it being shown on either occasion that the one affects the other. Often, such connections between concepts are taught years after the separate concepts themselves were introduced. A related tendency consists of the repetition of subject matter in successive grades without taking into account the complex and related events which, at the later age levels, may be successfully taught. A child may be taught about the Westward Movement four times during his school career without his ever learning about some of the more complex and subtle influences of other countries and cultures on the newly settled continent.

Memory functions often need attention in children with learning difficulties. Memory for verbal expression and semantic content are regarded as language functions. Memory for figural content is regarded as non-verbal and is therefore not included in the training of language; it is instead included in the perceptual training program. Memory functions are highly specific. Therefore, a great variety of tasks, some requiring verbal and others requiring motor reproduction, are necessary. It is desirable to encourage games in which the children have to verbally describe or illustrate with drawings events they have experienced. It may be helpful to require them to answer questions about events and experiences, and to have them recite assigned words, sentences, paragraphs, and poems. Number facts, spelling, and measurements constitute additional examples of valuable and highly discrete memory tasks.

Training in auditory discrimination is part of language training and involves perception of single sounds (isolated or in words), directed attention, and listening. Children must learn to attend, discriminate, and listen to the separate aspects of words, phrases, statements, questions, directions, and finally stories.

TRAINING IN HIGHER COGNITIVE PROCESSES

Techniques to develop higher cognitive processes can be integrated with the perceptual exercises discussed earlier. The ability to make inferences and form judgments is encouraged by the demands of a perceptual task when the latter is used by the teacher as a basis for discussion. For example, the picture of a train might lead to a consideration of why trains travel on tracks as contrasted with cars which travel on roads, or to a consideration of the relative speeds of trains, planes, and cars.

Many children have difficulties in imagery. Imagery can be enhanced through various perceptual tasks, or it can be imaginatively incorporated into the physical exercise program. Classification, serialization, and perception of relationships are basic to thought processes. These processes can be developed by means of such an activity as sorting forms and arranging them according to some perceptual scheme or logical order. Later, practice can be given in the completion of analogies, pictorial as well as verbal.[10, 11]

SOCIAL AND EMOTIONAL DEVELOPMENT

Skills in six broad developmental areas — sensory-motor functions, language, perception, higher thought processes, social adjustment, and emotional development — are essential if a child is to progress in learning. Thus far, we have discussed only the first four areas, but the guidance of a child's emotional and social development is obviously also of great importance for the final outcome of the educational effort. This seems to be true for the child with learning problems regardless of the origin of his disabilities. If the child is not enabled to make a good emotional and social adjustment, his role as a contributing member of society is seriously impaired. While the complexity of this topic precludes treatment here, it can be noted, however, that the enhancement of the child's abilities in the four previously discussed developmental areas will usually lead to a better level of emotional and social adjustment. Increases in motor skills, the ability to perceive the world as consistent and predictable, the understanding of spatial and temporal relationships, communicative ability, and success in solving problems, will normally lead to an enhanced self-concept and to better social adjustment.

SUMMARY

Research done at the Center and elsewhere strongly supports the view that children with learning difficulties frequently suffer from a multiplicity of disabilities, whatever the diagnostic category. Remediation is, therefore, most effective when the child's abilities and disabilities in all developmental areas are regarded as important determinants of the remedial program and when the child is provided with a variety of pertinent materials. The general approach described here entails the integration of visual-perceptual training with training in sensory-motor skills, language, and higher thought processes.

REFERENCES

1. de Hirsch, Katrina: *Predicting Reading Failure*. New York, Harper, 1966.
2. Frostig, Marianne; Lefever, D. W., and Whittlesey, J. R. B.: *The Marianne Frostig Developmental Test of Visual Perception*, 3rd ed. Palo Alto, Consulting Psychologists Press, 1964.
3. Frostig, Marianne, and Horne, D.: *The Frostig Program for the Development of Visual Perception*, pictures by Bea Mandell. Chicago, Follett, 1964.
4. Frostig, Marianne; Miller, A., and Horne, D.: *Teachers Guide to Beginning Pictures and Patterns*. Chicago, Follett, 1966.
5. Frostig, Marianne; Miller, A., and Horne, D.: *Intermediate Pictures and Patterns, Advanced Pictures and Patterns*. Chicago, Follett, 1967.
6. Gallagher, J. J.: Children with developmental imbalances: a psychoeducational definition. In Cruickshank, W. M. (Ed.): *The Teacher of Brain-Injured Children: A Discussion of the Bases for Competency*. New York, Syracuse, 1966, pp. 21-34.
7. Graubard, P. S.: Psycholinguistic Correlates of Reading Disability in Disturbed Children, presented at the American Psychological Association. New York, September 2, 1966.
8. Kass, Corrine E.: Psycholinguistic disabilities of children with reading problems. *Exceptional Child, 32:*533-9, 1966.
9. Kirk, S. A., and McCarthy, J. P.: *Illinois Test of Psycholinguistic Abilities*. Urbana, U of Ill, 1961.
10. Levi, Aurelia: Treatment of a disorder of perception and concept formation in a case of school failure. *J Consult Psychol, 29:*289-95, 1965.
11. Levi, Aurelia: Remedial techniques in disorders of concept formation. *J Special Ed, 1:*3-8, 1966.
12. Maslow, Phyllis; Frostig, Marianne; Lefever, D. W., and Whittlesey, J. R. B.: The Marianne Frostig developmental test of visual perception 1963 standardization. *Percept Motor Skills, 19* (2) :463-99, 1964.
13. Nicks, D. C., and Fleishman, E. A.: What do physical fitness tests measure? A review of factor analytic studies. *Educ and Psych Measurement, 22:*77-96, 1962.
14. Wepman, J. M.: *Wepman Test of Auditory Discrimination*. Chicago, Language Research Associates, 1958.

APPENDIX I

Difficulties as Assessed by Initial Basic Test Scores of 78 Children Referred to The Frostig Center Because of Learning Difficulties

Description of Sample

No children included who had known uncorrected sensory defects.

No children included with an initial evaluation of childhood psychosis.

Age range: 6 through 9 years. Mean chronological age was 7 years, 15 days.

All children had *either* verbal or performance WISC IQ scores of 78 or over. Mean full scale WISC IQ was 97.92; standard deviation 13.21.

Percentage Evidencing Difficulty with Visual Perception

(Subtest scale scores on Frostig Developmental Test of Visual Perception of 8 or below; Perceptual Quotient of 90 or below)
Subtest Scale Scores of 8 or below

Eye-Hand Coordination	60.3%
Figure-Ground Perception	71.8
Perception of Form Constancy	43.6
Perception of Position in Space	46.2
Perception of Spatial Relationships	30.8

Perceptual Quotient below 90   66.7%

Percentage Evidencing Difficulty with Auditory Perception

(Cutoff error scores below appropriate age norms established by Wepman Test of Auditory Discrimination)
    43.6%

Percentage Evidencing Difficulty with Language Functions

(Subtest and total language age scores .30 below standard score)
Subtest Scores .30 below Standard Score:

Auditory-Vocal Automatic	41.0%
Visual Decoding	28.2
Motor Encoding	37.2
Auditory-Vocal Association	46.2
Visual-Motor Sequencing	74.4
Vocal Encoding	48.7
Auditory-Vocal Sequencing	55.1
Visual-Motor Association	59.0
Auditory Decoding	19.2

Total Language Age .30 below Standard Score   53.8%

Percentage Evidencing Difficulty on WISC Subtests
(Subtest scale scores of 8 or below)

Information	52.6%
Comprehension	32.1
Arithmetic	46.2
Similarities	26.9
Vocabulary	26.9
Digit Span	38.5
Picture Completion	30.8
Picture Arrangement	35.9
Block Design	28.2
Object Assembly	42.3
Coding	48.7

APPENDIX II

SOME TRAINING PROCEDURES BASED ON
THE ILLINOIS TEST OF PSYCHOLINGUISTIC ABILITIES

Subtest Name	Example	Functions Covered	Training Procedures
Auditory-Vocal Automatic	Pictures: "Here is an apple, here are two ----?" (apples)	Ability to speak grammatically. This is automatic because child not taught formally but learns through imitation. Taps imitative, memory abilities.	Choral reading. Modified repetition games. Opportunity for child to express ideas. Adult conversation with children.
Visual Decoding	Child is shown picture, e.g., a nail; then must find, from among four other pictures (screw, hammer, tack, and pen) an object with similar function. (Tack is the correct answer to the example.)	Ability to comprehend pictures and to form concepts. Functional identities are tapped.	Have children describe and interpret pictures. Sorting tasks in which underlying principle should be verbalized. Use of maps, charts, etc.
Motor Encoding	Child is shown object or picture and must *show* how it is used, e.g., a pencil sharpener. The child must act out use, without any verbalization, employing correct spatial and temporal movements.	Ability to express ideas through movement and gesture.	Have child act out instructions or do what educational therapist does. Charades and role playing. Learning everyday activities. Have child demonstrate ideas.
Auditory-Vocal Association	Verbal analogies: "I cut with a saw, I pound with a —. (hammer)	Ability to relate words meaningfully. Taps verbal concepts of a more automatic sort than vocal encoding.	Making good associations—games of opposites, finding relationships between words, finding differences or the one that does not belong between several things.

Visual-Motor Sequencing	Pictures of objects or geometric shapes are put one by one in front of child, then mixed up—he must select pictures and reproduce correct sequence	Memory for a visual sequence.	Copy bead series from memory. Reproduce patterns from memory. Complete a visual series. Encourage visualization—remember what seen and the order seen.
Vocal Encoding	Child is shown object and told, "Tell me *all* about it," e.g., a ball.	Taps verbal fluency and number of concepts child can employ (taps divergent thinking). Ability to express ideas in words.	Encourage child to verbalize ideas—ask for wide variety of uses, observations, origins of things. Sharing times, storytelling, etc.
Auditory-Vocal Sequencing	Child is told series of numbers and must repeat them in same order.	Test of immediate recall for digits. Auditory memory tapped.	Repeat and complete an auditory sequence as, 'One, two, three, ——?" Repeat a series of sounds or words or phrases. Games in which more and more ideas are added on—"I went to the store, I bought candy, ——". (candy, peanuts, etc.)
Visual-Motor Association	Child is shown picture, then finds one of four other pictures that "goes with" the first.	Ability to comprehend functional relationships—a pencil "goes with" a scratch pad.	Sorting of objects, classifying by use (origin, construction, color, form, etc.) Awareness and verbalization of principle categorization.
Auditory Decoding	Answer "yes" or "no" questions, e.g., "Do cars cry?"	Receptive understanding of spoken language. Imagery, vocabulary and information also tapped, also ability to attend.	Answering questions. Following verbal directions. Listening to stories. Reading comprehension exercises. Games where clues are given.

*Table drawn by Janet Switzer, Ph.D.

APPENDIX III

FROSTIG DEVELOPMENTAL TEST OF VISUAL PERCEPTION
AND RELATED TRAINING PROCEDURES

(Brief Summary; see Teacher's Guide)

Sub-test name	Example	Functions covered	Training procedures
Eye-Motor Coordination	Draw straight lines horizontally. Stop and start on target.	Eye-hand coordination. Necessary for hand-writing, drawing, arts and crafts, manipulatory and self-help activities.	Eye movement training, Arts and crafts, Manipulatory exercises, Handwriting exercises, Physical education program, Frostig worksheets
Figure-Ground	Find a hidden figure. Find one of two or several intersecting figures.	Ability to focus visually on relevant aspects of visual field and "tune out" irrelevant background.	"Finding" games, Sorting exercises, Frostig worksheets
Form Constancy	Find all the squares on a page regardless of color, background, tilt, size.	Ability to see sameness of essential form despite image on retina. Has implication for learning to identify letters presented in various prints.	Identify objects or drawings at different distances or angles. Draw diagrams of 3-dimensional patterns. Find all objects of a certain shape in the room. Frostig worksheets

FROSTIG DEVELOPMENTAL TEST OF VISUAL PERCEPTION
AND RELATED TRAINING PROCEDURES (continued)

(Brief Summary; see Teacher's Guide)

Sub-test name	Examples	Functions covered	Training procedures
Position in Space	Find the form which is reversed or rotated.	Ability to discriminate position; to differentiate letters such as "d" and "b," "w" and "m"	Exercises promoting awareness of body position to objects--go under the table, over the chair, around the desk, etc. Physical education program Learning directions in space: right, left. Frostig worksheets
Spatial Relations	Duplicate a dot pattern by linking dots with a line.	Ability to see spatial relationships of objects to one another related to ability to perceive the sequence of letters in a word.	Copy patterns with pegs, beads, marbles; puzzles; Description of spatial relationships of one object to another; Frostig worksheets; spelling and writing.

APPENDIX IV
BASIC TEST RESULTS

NAME _____ BIRTH DATE _____ C.A. _____ DATE _____

Test	Subject Category	Adequate or Above	Training Needed	Date Given
Visual Perception				
I	Eye Motor Coordination			
II	Figure Ground			
III	Form Constancy			
IV	Position in Space			
V	Spatial Relations			
Auditory Perception				
Wepman				
Wechsler Intelligence Scale for Children				
I	Information			
II	Comprehension			
III	Arithmetic			
IV	Similarities			
V	Vocabulary			
VI	Digit Span			
VII	Picture Completion			
VIII	Picture Arrangement			
IX	Block Design			
X	Object Assembly			
XI	Coding			
I.T.P.A.				
VII	Auditory-Vocal Automatic			
II	Visual Decoding			
VI	Motor Encoding			
III	Auditory-Vocal Association			
IX	Visual-Motor Sequencing			
V	Vocal Encoding			
VIII	Auditory-Vocal Sequencing			
IV	Visual-Motor Association			
I	Auditory Decoding			

Perceptual Quotient=

Verbal I.Q. =
Performance I.Q. =
Full Scale I.Q. =

Actual Grade =
Arithmetic =
Spelling =
Reading =

Sensory Motor Development

ITPA Total Language Age =

X

CURRICULUM DEVELOPMENT FOR CHILDREN WITH BRAIN DAMAGE

BLUMA B. WEINER

INCREASING AWARENESS OF DIFFERENCES within as well as between individual children has contributed not only to an acceleration of academic interest in the developmental problems of those who have been designated, in various terms, as "children with minimal brain damage," but also to an extension of efforts to provide educational services for them. Such programs, which began as private clinical ventures or carefully delineated institutional or university projects, may now be found in the domain of public as well as private enterprise and under the aegis of a remarkable multiplicity of disciplines. It would not be impossible to locate, at least in the United States, facilities for "brain-injured children" which owe their existence to the initiative and continued active participation of members of the health, psychological, and social service professions as well as to representatives of the several educational specialties. Various symptoms have brought these children to the attention of practitioners in physical medicine, pediatrics, neurology, psychiatry, and ophthalmology and optometry. Investigators in clinical, developmental, and experimental psychology have been particularly interested in specific aspects of perceptual and conceptual learning in such children. Social workers with public and private agencies, including some with religious affiliation, have been involved with diverse situational problems growing out of their management. Among educators, sponsors of programs may be found among persons whose concern was a projection of their work with mentally retarded, cerebral-palsied, language and speech handicapped, and seriously emotionally disturbed children, as well as among those with primary interest in instructional areas such as reading. Parents of brain-damaged children have also been instrumental in obtaining community recognition and action, and in conveying both to professional and to general audiences the nature and immediacy of their needs.

However, in spite of some very well-intended efforts, the extent and quality of present services for children with minimal brain damage is decidedly uneven. It must be acknowledged that any program of special educational services encounters certain kinds of obstacles which also affect the general educational system — shortages of personnel and of budget, and an inertia which sometimes is difficult to distinguish from apathy. However, this discussion is not focused on lags in social and institutional change as such, but rather centers on matters which appear to have relevance to the improvement of services that now exist and influence the readiness of communities to respond to appeals to reason and to conscience.

Efforts to educate minimally brain-damaged children have been reminiscent of the fable of the blind men and the elephant. Depending upon which portion of the pachyderm's anatomy came within the reach of his investigators, he "was like" a huge leaf waving in the breeze, a broad table top, a short dangling rope, a twisting snake, a wide wall, a tree trunk, or a spear. Only the sighted observer was in a position to know what the animal looked like *in toto*, both as a specimen of his kind and in comparison to other species; only his keeper was in a position to appreciate the behavioral uniqueness of the animal as an individual elephant. To pursue the analogy, it is suggested that attention needs to be directed toward two specific professional inadequacies which constitute a lack of "vision" and thus act as obstacles to our knowledge of these children and to the effectiveness of our efforts to help them. One such deficiency resides in the skewness as well as the skimpiness of "special" professional preparation, while the other derives from unimaginative accommodation to conventional views of *curriculum*. Fortunately these conditions may be modified since they are essentially functions of lapses in interdisciplinary communication instead of being irreversible structural faults.

THE NEED FOR BROADER KNOWLEDGE AND INTEREST

The task of educating the child with minimal brain damage requires a repertoire of information, insights, and competencies which draws across arbitrary lines of professional proprietorship, especially in the several areas which have been identified as *special education.* The minimally brain-damaged child, as well as other handicapped children, can benefit from the application of concepts, procedures, and materials which have customarily been viewed as the exclusive "stock-in-trade" of one or another of the educational or service specialities that have been mentioned. A renaissance of thought and ethic has already begun; the vanguard of creative, responsible leadership has encouraged and facilitated an interchange of ideas which will ultimately augment and improve the basic preservice and continuing inservice preparation of teachers, administrators, and others who work directly with programs for disabled children.

Common understanding and, to some extent, a sharing of expertise in certain aspects of behavioral and instructional evaluation and management are not only desirable but also are inevitable sequels to accurate perception of the particular requirements of such children and to intellectually honest appraisals of the resourcefulness of individual practitioners. Thus, the ways in which notions of "islands of health," "ego strength," and "structure" are interpreted by persons who work with seriously emotionally handicapped children, and the theoretical foundations and specific procedural techniques which have been formulated by educators who work with "dyslexic" children may also have application to brain-damaged children as well as to others who bear different diagnostic labels. Teachers of children with different kinds of disabilities have much to learn from each other; that they have not yet done so has been in part a reflection of the kind of immaturity and provincialism which isolation tends to perpetuate. The most damaging effect is the reduction of interest in problems that appear to be "out-of-bounds" and that blur the idealized picture of a clear-cut, uncomplicated handicap. Thus the existence of some degree of mental retardation in children with other disabilities is often denied or dismissed as not worthy of serious consideration.

Educators of children with sensory or major physical handicaps have frequently excluded from consideration those children who have associated deficits in intellectual functioning, while mentally retarded children with behavioral and emotional disorders have, for the most part, been ignored as educationally or therapeutically unpromising. These considerations are of particular relevance in any discussion of the education of minimally brain-damaged children, who are by no means a clear-cut diagnostically identifiable segment of the child population.

Among professional persons who give the matter any sustained thought, it would be generally acknowledged that the need is pressing for sensible and defensible educational management of the children whom we have been calling minimally brain-damaged. The very act of diagnostic labelling has often served as a signal for obscuring the individual identity of a child and for endowing him with a stereotyped "mystique" — a set of behavioral and learning characteristics which may or may not be valid in his particular case. Semi-informed adults, including professional people as well as parents, have frequently assumed that the tag "brain damaged" refers to a unique syndrome which requires an exclusive and specific set of regulations for its containment. However, Birch[1] has efficiently differentiated between the *fact* of brain damage and the *concept* of brain damage, and he has clearly identified the main confusion which has resulted from various semantic somersaults. He states,

> It is essential that we recognize that the disturbed behavior seen in the clinic is not "due to" brain damage as such. We never see an individual whose disturbed behavior is a direct consequence of his brain damage. Instead, we see individuals with damage to the nervous system, which may have resulted in some primary disorganization, who have developed patterns of behavior in the course of atypical relations with the developmental environment, including the interpersonal, objective, and social features. The behavioral disturbances of children who come to our notice are developmental products and not merely manifestations of a damaged portion of the brain.

Working from this viewpoint, it seems axiomatic that detailed consideration should be given to the *developmental environment,* including those features which fall within the purview of formal school provisions. During the past twenty years, a few pioneers — notably Strauss and Lehtinen, Kephart, Gellner, Cruickshank, and Frostig — have advanced insightful and ingenious procedures for the experimental instruction of brain-injured children. Their clinical work and research have stimulated further investigations and developments by others. It is precisely because of the increasing activity that has been generated in this area of inquiry that particular care should be given to the overall total educational planning for these children. Well-meaning, enthusiastically but carelessly conceived programs of instructional "adjustments" without valid conceptual orientation or provision for appropriate control and evaluation, result in unproductive, monotonous, even depressing tasks that lack continuity and direction and that substitute proliferation for progression.

The education of the brain-damaged child, like the education of any handicapped child, should entail provisions for rehabilitation of functions which have been impaired; allowance also should be made for stimulation of normal functions, for the acquisition of information and skills which are commensurate with the child's general level of maturation, and for the development of appropriate social values, attitudes, and responses. In substance, the brain-damaged child should have the benefit of expert, comprehensive, responsibly managed educational treatment. Such management would provide for particularized instruction and assistance in areas of specific learning difficulty or disorder but would not neglect intact functions nor disregard the motivating and integrating potentialities of other areas of content.

Because so little notice has been given to the concept of a comprehensive educational program for brain-damaged children, and because school is presumably intended to be a major landmark in their developmental environment, the time is certainly at hand to make such an effort. It seems especially important to try to interpret the contents and functions of the early elementary school curriculum (nursery through grade six) in such a way that their special significance for these children is clearly represented.

Birch[1] has summarized the behavioral symptoms which frequently form the base for referral of children of school age. The symptoms commonly considered to be diagnostic criteria for assignment of children to the "brain-damaged" category are disordered behavior, short attention span, emotional lability, social incompetence, defective work habits, impulsiveness and meddlesomeness, and specific learning disorders. The degree to which one or more of these "symptoms" is manifested varies greatly from child to child, and the particular ways in which they may be expressed are manifold. Variable also are the levels of irritation which can be tolerated at home and in an ordinary classroom. The role of the "managing educator" is not going to be a simple or easy one. He must attempt to educate the child "out of" as well as in spite of any one or more of such disconcerting difficulties.

ANOTHER VIEW OF CURRICULUM

For the purpose of this discussion, the term *curriculum* denotes the scope and implies the progressive sequence of the several instructional experiences which are commonly offered to children enrolled in school programs from the nursery or preschool period through grade six. Although nursery school and kindergarten classes are not yet universally established features of American public school education, their potential contribution to the developmental environment is increasingly acknowledged, especially for handicapped and other seriously disadvantaged children. Traditionally, school curriculum offerings are designated in terms of formal subject or content areas, such as *language arts, mathematics, social studies, science, physical education, art,* and *music,* although a rather amorphous nomenclature is employed for nursery and kindergarten classes. In order to dramatize the potential relevance of the common school curriculum to the *development* of children, and to make more explicit some of its possible and desirable applications to the education of minimally brain-damaged children, a somewhat unorthodox formulation is used here.

Under the headings of *communication, behavioral tools, informational agenda, spatial and quantitative understanding and skills, and self-actualization,* reference points have been determined for the examination of curriculum content in terms of potential functional equivalence for several aspects of human growth and development. Specifically, attention is drawn to perceptual, motor, conceptual, and emotional and social learning. Such a conception of curriculum is not widely expressed by persons who work with minimally brain-damaged children. The present formulation is an invitation to look at and to devise fresh ways of employing stable features of the developmental environment.

One of the conventional views of school curriculum holds that the *cultural heritage* should be preserved and passed on to succeeding generations of children. This position is challenged when children with severe learning and behavioral disorders appear for instruction. Although it is challenged, it is not automatically negated. Rather, it should be pursued further; passed on for what purpose? Both general and special educators have frequently lost sight of the fact that the so-called cultural heritage is a product of irregular but continual selection and rejection of content over a long period of time, and that the functions which have been noted here are the underlying rationale for such selection and retention.

The curriculum content which has survived, particularly the common features of nursery-elementary school education enumerated earlier, has presumably been retained for the contribution it is expected to make to *human* survival and advancement. Thus, curriculum should be regarded not as the "vessel" in which knowledge is contained and transmitted, but rather as *one* "channel" by which the cultural heritage becomes instrumental in the educational process. For no group of children is such a conceptualization of curriculum better-advised than for those who are regarded as handicapped. The sometimes puzzling, often paradoxical situations which are encountered in efforts to educate various categories of handicapped children, especially those with minimal brain damage, are partially accounted for by inadequate perception of the instrumental power of the school curriculum as well as by our incomplete knowledge of and procedures for dealing with specific learning disorders.

It is proposed that sustained attention to the points noted above, and systematic and persistent efforts to develop a functionally interpreted curriculum could bring into existence special services of quality and integrity, not only for the particular children under consideration here but also for all children who pose unusual problems in education and rehabilitation. The speculations which follow are an extension of work begun at the Children's Residential and Day Treatment Service of the Western Pennsylvania Psychiatric Institute and Clinic, under the sponsorship of the Graduate Programs in Child Care and Child Development, University of Pittsburgh School of Medicine.

Communication

The usual view of the *language arts* or *communication* area embraces hearing and listening, speaking, reading, writing, and spelling. More elaborate achievements in spoken and written language depend upon their acquisition. But underpinning these foundations are even more primary processes: accurate and stable auditory, visual, tactile, and kinesthetic functions of reception, perception, association, integration and retention, and dependable motor, visual-motor, and vocal coordinations. Difficulty with any of these processes constitutes potential impediment to achievement in more complex school tasks, not only in the language arts *per se,* but also in many other aspects of the school program. Most serious and damaging are the obstructions to effective social interaction with parents and peers.

The emphasis upon visual-perceptual functioning in so many educational programs for brain-damaged children is a response to *one* of these considerations. Whether it is always an appropriate response depends upon the adequacy of the diagnostic evaluation in each case *and* on the progress which the child has already made. There may be a greater, more fundamental need for work with other processes or areas of dysfunction, particularly auditory and associative difficulties. Coping with transitory auditory stimuli poses some exceedingly perplexing and frustrating problems both for the child who experiences the disorder and for the people who live and work with him. The contributions of Kirk and Mc-Carthy[3] and their associates, in developing and standardizing the *Illinois Test of Psycholinguistic Abilities,* and in emphasizing clinical teaching procedures derived from a communication model, have excited and encouraged much fresh work in this direction. So, too, has the work of Myklebust, Barry, and McGin-nis, who for many years have developed insights and field-tested procedures for working with children with various types of aphasias.

Behavioral Tools

Nursery and kindergarten teachers have understood for a long time that children have to learn how to become "school children." This observation is particularly applicable to the brain-damaged child of any age who is going to school, especially for the first time. Certain behaviors must be established for effective participation; when these responses are not already present, they must be considered as legitimate parts of the curriculum.

Frequently the young or even the preadolescent brain-damaged child may need some help (quite literally some "instruction") in learning the *meaning* and acquiring the *motions* of behaviors which are often taken for granted: *looking at, listening to, waiting, taking turns, trying, helping, sharing,* and *working.* He may have to be guided by appropriate verbalizations, demonstrations, and going-through-the motions in his development of meaning and reinforcement of positive valence toward such behavioral expectancies. Knowing how to behave under certain conditions, particularly in the classroom, provides the bases for establishing the inner controls needed to cope with one's own labile impulses or comparatively low threshold of tolerance for competing attractions. The acquisition of such controls assists the brain-damaged child, as well as other children, to assume and carry on successfully his "role" as a school child. The importance of this task should not be overlooked.

The brain-damaged child may be assigned to a particular niche or "status" in his family and neighborhood without there being any clearly defined or consistent and developmentally constructive behavioral demands made of him. He may be perceived as *the baby, the sick one,* or as Lewis suggests, *the other one.* Or, while he may be regarded as *son, brother,* or *neighbor's child,* these roles and their appropriate functions are not always quite clear to his parents, his brothers and sisters, or to the neighbors.

On the other hand, the role of school child is fairly well-defined, and it can be understood by children as young as three years. Expectations which are established for the various age groups are reasonably stable and reasonably "reasonable." There is a progression in the role functions which is intrinsically rewarding for most children; the child who masters various tasks at one level moves on to the next task, group, room, or grade where he learns to do more complicated and potentially more interesting and satisfying activities. The development of competency in the use of "behavioral tools" contributes not only to the effectiveness of achievement in the more traditional aspects of school curriculum, but also to the evolution of purpose or motivation for anticipated tasks. It is exceedingly important for the brain-damaged child to learn that "tomorrow will be better," and to expect and to be eager to work hard for that desirable change. A solid command of the basic tools for making and meeting such changes gives him something to "go for" and, more significantly, something to "grow for."

Informational Agenda

All children require some kind of assistance in becoming aware of and in dealing with various natural and social phenomena. These conceptual aspects of experience are important "informational agenda" of nursery, kindergarten, and elementary school education. They are data to be acquired, understood, and incorporated as comfortably as possible into the expanding universe of one's knowledge of one's own self and of other persons and things. In more conventional terms, such information is labelled *social studies* (or history and geography, etc.) and *science* (or nature study, health and safety, etc.) .

Children need accurate information about many aspects of the physical world and the social groups in which they live. They need information about plants and animals, about weather and seasons, about things on the ground, in the ground, beneath the ground, and above the surface and atmosphere of the earth. They need to know about other persons and other groups of persons, about things to eat and things to wear, and about nearby and faraway places. They need to know how people get from one place to another, how they live and work, and how they send messages and goods to one another. Children need information about visible and tangible things and about matters which are not visible or tangible — about thoughts and feelings, and about relationships between themselves and others. Such information and the means for handling it are acquired gradually, often laboriously, and sometimes painfully, in many ways and situations. School is a place where these observations can be augmented, corrected, and organized.

It cannot be assumed categorically that a brain-damaged child has a greater or lesser need for information than do other children. However, one must consider the possibility that such a child may have more than ordinary difficulties in acquiring or dealing with information. He may have difficulties with his data-gathering or with his data processing because of one or more of the disabling conditions noted in the discussion of communication. Or, simply because he is still a child and a relatively inexperienced human being, he may respond to certain information with elation, amusement, disbelief, shock, denial, matter-of-factness, or indifference. The brain-damaged child, like any of his age peers, would be at a disadvantage if he were uninformed about commonly known events and relationships and acceptable ways of responding to them. Such knowledge is not only a basis for social exchange; it is a substructure for knowing and being at ease in the world of actuality.

Nothing has been claimed here for the acquisition of formally organized information as a step toward other school achievements at a later date. Instead, concern has been expressed for those functions which are ends in themselves and which tend to confirm and reward the effort of learning. Such concern appears to appraise more realistically the actual issues which are entailed in formal education and which are too often obscured for the normal as well as for the exceptional child.

Spatial and Quantitative Understanding and Skill

Very careful attention needs to be given to processes which precede rote enumeration and computation. Awareness of one's self as a distinct entity, and of one's body members, digits, and facial features has been advanced as necessary for the meaningful acquisition of more formal operations. Perception of units, groups, mass, direction, and distance — and their comparative relationships — are the foundations upon which children learn how to locate and manipulate themselves, other persons, and objects in space and in time. The many categories of spatial and quantitative percepts and concepts, and the verbal and visual symbols for their appearance and functions are valid curriculum content, and the processes by which competencies are acquired are facilitated and verified by manual explorations and operations.

Introduction of the new mathematics and the availability of several experimental systems suggest interesting possibilities as well as problems in the education of brain-damaged children. Whatever "system" may be adopted, certain practical tasks of daily life will persist, and they will require spatial and quantitative understanding and skill: rational counting and grouping, locating in space (*in, on, under, over, beside, before, behind*), reckoning (not simply "telling") time, and using money. These demands, as well as others of similar character, begin in early childhood and continue throughout life. Provision for systematic, rational instruction and appropriate reinforcement is viewed as an important part of the school curriculum for all children. Methods of instruction, especially for children who are handicapped, should insure perceptual accuracy, correct terminology, and frequent realistic social application.

Self-Actualization

Many students of human development have been concerned with the infant's initial task of becoming aware of himself as a creature, separate from his surroundings, who is comprised of a variety of parts which stay put together in a dependable way and yet are capable of an exciting and satisfying repertoire of performances. But this achievement is just a prologue to the larger, lifelong drama of self-realization and "actualization." The brain-damaged child, like other children, participates in a continuous complexity of behaviors which increase and deepen his perceptions of himself as a person, and his appreciation and enjoyment of the person who is himself. Jersild[2] in particular has reported in simple, economical terminology that among the various aspects of "self" are *perceptual, conceptual,* and *attitudinal* components. Omission of any of these phenomena from the management of the "developmental environment" of the brain-damaged child would distort our perspective of his problems and of our responsibilities, and would deprive him of his strongest potential asset: his sense of being regarded as a person who is capable of growth and of active engagement in the promotion of that growth.

In addition to those aspects of curriculum which have already been mentioned, there are others which offer fruitful opportunities for developing functions that contribute to general fitness, pride and pleasure in mastery, and social interaction. In particular, physical education, arts and crafts, and music have long been recognized not only as pleasant divertissements but also as means for involving the "whole" person in powerful activity. This knowledge is almost as ancient as civilization, and connoisseurs as well as cranks have made use of it. Sensitive but unsentimental choices from among the incalculable number of potential forms of overt activity can make capital gains out of direct sensory and motor responses.

Physical Education

Numerous activities have been brought within the general meaning of *physical education* and made to serve a variety of developmental, corrective, recreational, and social purposes. Certain aspects of physical development, such as posture, balance, coordination, and dexterity have received some attention in individual programs of corrective prescriptions for brain-damaged children.

Application of the arts and science of physical and occupational therapy has sometimes been included for children who demonstrated difficulties with "body-image," "directionality," and "distractibility" as well as for children who required some assistance in acquiring facility in locomotion or other self-help activities of daily living. Here again is a large sphere of technical professional knowledge to which teachers of brain-damaged children need access.

The developmental, recreational, and social aspects of physical education for these children have too often been ignored. It may be that this neglect is mainly a function of the restricted, make-shift facilities which are available for their use. Or, it may be that this phase of instruction is left deliberately for out-of-school hours as a time-filler. For purposes of comprehensive educational management, however, these uses of physical education activities should be examined and evaluated. The managing educator of the brain damaged child has to be prepared to advise on many extra curricular as well as curricular matters.

Brain-damaged children, like other children, require vigorous physical activities of various kinds to promote overall strength, endurance, and general well-being. The discriminating choice and regulation of those activities, as well as others which facilitate the acquisition of specific skills in individual and group enterprises, encourages the processes of self-actualization. The child is enabled to judge himself under favorable conditions which provide him with a fair chance to succeed or to learn from failure when his efforts fall short of criterion.

He also has opportunity to acquire individual competencies which can serve as recreational satisfactions in and out of school-time and long after his school days are over. Skills such as swimming, dancing, and bowling, and knowledgeability of popular games provide foundations for later interests, either as a direct participant or as an appreciative spectator. The brain-damaged child, or any child, who acquires a stock of common competencies strengthens the chances for personal enjoyment and self-satisfaction. From the early introduction of simple body movements and stunts, through the use of carefully chosen equipment and the introduction of sports and games, a carefully planned program of physical education contributes substantively to all aspects of self-actualization.

Arts and Crafts

The materials and processes of arts and crafts activities embrace an extraordinary range of possibilities. They offer correspondingly wide and heterogeneous opportunities for perceptual and conceptual development as well as for mastery of skills and pleasure in performance. Exploration and manipulation of visual and tactual matter through seeing, touching, grasping, moving, changing, and using are illustrations of the data-gathering and data-processing referred to earlier. Using the fingers and hands as well as tools, utensils, and miscellaneous instruments and supplies, enables the brain-damaged child to validate visual impressions or to correct them, and to test his judgment and his competencies. These aspects of *art education* are ordinarily overlooked and eclipsed by the familiar global and stereotyped views of art as expression, therapy, recreation or vocational education.

In many, perhaps most, classes for brain-damaged children, the entire range of art activity is viewed with reservation, and *art* often is presented as a task of visual-motor pursuit such as tracing, connecting broken lines, making step-by-step and dot-to-dot "pictures," or reproduction of simple linear designs. Sometimes, as a special treat or as an adjunct to an arithmetic lesson, a child may be permitted to spend a little time with a lump of non-messy modeling material. Or, as a concession to "recreation" or the advent of Mother's Day, he may even be allowed the use of a looper loom. Acquiring solid familiarity with the substantive aspects of arts and crafts could open an astonishing number of alternate choices to the educator of brain-damaged children. His responsibility for the selection and regulation of instrumental stimuli would not be abrogated. Instead, he would have at his disposal a more detailed and specific knowledge of the potential stimulus value of various materials and procedures. Because art education as such occupies such an insignificant place in our total educational economy, few teachers are well-enough prepared to steer a confident course between the Scylla of "free expression" and the Charybdis of immediate utility. Both views of art activity are shortsighted and distorted. Encounters with graphic and plastic media, with visual and spatial tasks of composition and construction, and with cause-and-effect sequences of particular procedures, are instrumental in the process of self-actualization. They provide the human creature with means and with meanings for growing up.

Music

The qualities of sound and their influence upon the behavior of man and beast have been recognized for centuries, and the special arrangements of sounds which are called *music* have been employed in many ways to soothe or stir the human spirit and body. In one form or another, *music education* has become part of the curricula of early childhood and elementary school programs. Emphasis is usually placed upon group instruction in body rhythms, on singing, and — for the older "elect" — on instrumental performance. As in the earlier comments on physical education and arts and crafts, attention is focused here upon those properties of music which provide unique foundations for self-actualization as it has been defined for this discussion: for creating awareness of external as well as internal states and readiness to engage in their exploration, and for the facilitation of responses which make that engagement rewarding.

In the earlier observations on *communication,* it was indicated that accurate and stable auditory perception is a prime condition of language development in normal children. (In the case of seriously hearing-handicapped children, accurate and stable visual, tactile, and kinesthetic perceptions are the instrumental conditions.) There is substantial clinical evidence that some brain-damaged children are disabled by certain types of auditory problems. There is also evidence that others are handicapped not by an identifiable impairment or disorder, but by a seeming indifference to sounds made by human voices or even to grosser environmental sounds. Whether their unresponsiveness may be attributed to neurological factors, or whether it is a psychological "shutting out" is not easy to determine. However, the tools and instruments of music offer strategic possibilities for modifying such behavior as well as for enabling "normal" listeners to become more perceptive. The qualities of music — rhythm, volume, pitch, tone, and pattern or melody — are demonstrable, and they are responsive not only to the manipulations of adults but also to the controls of quite young children. Furthermore, the variety of music-making instruments in addition to the human voice is limited only by the ingenuity of the adult and his tolerance for the unconventional. It is the *physics* rather than the formal aesthetics of music which hold the most promise for educational payoff at this stage of endeavor. Observations of children from the "pot-and-pan" to the "Beatle-fan" status tend to confirm this impression.

THE DIMENSIONS OF EDUCABILITY

Although the concept of educability is implicit in all programs of special school services for handicapped children, it has never been clearly defined. The nearest approximation of a definition which is not tautological, i.e. the "capacity for being educated," is the differentiation which has been made between "educable" and "trainable" mentally retarded children. While that distinction is not entirely satisfactory, it does bring attention to certain aspects of school progress which may appropriately be labeled "dimensions" of education. These dimensions are *level* and *rate* of achievement in a *range* of educationally and socially relevant behavior. *Level* refers to the total amount of development or achievement and is usually expressed in terms of age or grade norms. *Rate* refers to the *time* it required to attain that level or a specific amount of gain. *Range* refers not to the statistical concept but to the concept of *territory* in which achievement has been made.

It is not a simple or easy matter to prepare and maintain helpful descriptive reports on the school progress of handicapped children, especially for children who are mentally retarded, seriously emotionally disturbed, or disabled by specific functional disorders. The criteria of age or grade levels are not always meaningful in these circumstances, nor do the conditions of instruction always lend themselves to the detection of month-by-month increments. An additional problem is created when a severely limited school program curtails the range of possible performance and thus reduces even further the opportunities for and the kinds of observations that need to be made.

In spite of all these difficulties, the curriculum content outlined in the preceding pages is relevant to the development of the child with minimal brain damage, and useful systems of observing and recording his progress in the several areas of instruction can and should be established. In addition to the dimensions of *level, rate,* and *range,* two others should be included: *efficiency* and *autonomy.* The term *efficiency* refers to the degree of correctness or accuracy of the child's responses, and the term *autonomy* refers to the degree of his independence in approaching and executing tasks set before him and tasks which he has set for himself. Observations on an appropriate range of curriculum experiences — along the dimensions of level, rate, efficiency, and autonomy — would contribute substantively to a body of evidence on educational achievement. The accumulating, organizing, and collating of such information on a child with minimal brain damage — or on any handicapped child — takes into account the reality of intra-individual differences and is more useful than the generalized unitary terms of *educable* or *ineducable.* As the child is assisted in the acquision of competency in the several areas which have been described here *(communication, behavioral tools, informational agenda, spatial and qualitative understanding and skill, and self-actualization)*, the nature and extent of his educability become manifest.

REFERENCES

1. Birch, H. G. (Ed.) : *Brain Damage in Children. The Biological and Social Aspects.* Baltimore, Williams & Wilkins, 1964, pp. 8, 10-11.
2. Jersild, A. T.: *Child Psychology,* 5th ed. Englewood-Cliffs, Prentice-Hall, 1960, p. 116.
3. Kirk, S. A., and McCarthy, J. J.: *Illinois Test of Psycholinguistic Abilities,* Experimental Edition. Urbana, University of Illinois, 1961.

NAME INDEX

Ades, H. W., 50, 57
Adler, S., 60
Allen, R. M., 79, 87, 92
Amatruda, C. S., 42
Anastasi, A., 79, 92
Appleby, S. V., 61
Arick, B. E., 61
Arnold, G., 60

Bangs, E., 60
Barger, W. C., 60
Barr, B., 48, 57
Barry, H., 57, 251
Bensberg, G. J., 220, 221
Bentzen, F. A., 192, 221
Berry, M. F., 20, 21, 22, 23, 42
Bickford, R. G., 60
Birch, H. G., 10, 72, 74, 75, 79, 92, 93, 108, 220, 246, 248, 260
Blacketer-Simmonds, D. A., 92
Blakely, R. W., 60
Bloomer, H., 57
Bocca, E., 50, 51, 54, 57
Bordley, J., 48, 55, 57
Bortner, M., 10, 74, 92, 108
Boshes, B., 62
Bradley, B. H., 220
Bradley, W. H., 60
Brinker, C. H., 61
Briskey, R. J., 62
Brutten, M., 56, 58
Burgemeister, B., 87, 92
Buros, O. K., 79, 87, 91, 92

Calearo, C., 54, 57
Cantor, G. N., 220
Capobianco, R. J., 220
Chess, S., 93, 108
Clements, S. D., 10, 93
Clevenger, L. J., 220
Cody, D. T. R., 60

Connor, L. E., 60
Coursin, D., 61
Critchley, M., 93
Cromwell, R. L., 221
Cruickshank, W. M., 192, 193, 221, 247

Davis, H., 55, 58, 60
De Hirsch, K., 235
Demb, H., 92
Denhoff, E., 15, 42, 108
Di Carlo, L. M., 49, 58, 60
Dix, M. R., 58
Doctor, P. V., 58
Doerfler, L. G., 61
Doster, M. E., 61
Dougherty, A., 61
Douglas, F. M., 58
Downs, M., 61
Duffy, J. K., 61
Dunn, L. M., 192

Eagles, R. L., 61
Ehrenreich, D. L., 16, 43
Einstein, A., 152
Eisenberg, L., 72, 93
Eisenberg, R., 61
Eisenson, J., 20, 21, 22, 23, 42
Epps, H. O., 201, 202, 206, 213, 221
Ewing, A. W. B., 48, 58, 61
Ewing, I. R., 48, 58

Feldman, I. S., 6, 10
Filling, S., 61
Fleishman, E. A., 235
Foshee, J. G., 221
Fowler, E. P., Jr., 58, 59, 61
Frazier, T. M., 61
Frisina, R. D., 47, 54, 58, 61
Frostig, M., 235, 240, 247
Furth, H. G., 93

261

Galambos, R., 58
Gallagher, J. J., 7, 10, 75, 93, 221, 227, 235
Gellner, L., 193, 194, 195, 196, 197, 198, 199, 201, 218, 219, 220, 221, 247
Gesell, A., 42
Goldstein, K., 20, 21, 22, 23, 42, 75, 93, 133
Goldstein, R., 49, 56, 58, 59, 60, 61, 62
Goodhill, V., 58
Goodman, W. S., 61
Graham, J. T., 63
Graubard, P. S., 226, 235
Griffin, E., 61
Grings, W. M., 61
Guggenbuehl, J., 205

Haeussermann, E., 79, 93
Hagberg, B., 15, 28, 43
Hagen, E., 94
Hallpike, C. S., 58
Halstead, W. C., 133, 146
Hardy, J. B., 61
Hardy, W. G., 57, 61
Harris, R., 61
Henson, A. R., 58
Hermelin, B., 10
Hertzig, M. E., 93
Hillis, J. W., 62
Hirsh, I., 58
Honnard, R. R., 61
Horne, D., 235
Hubel, D. H., 51, 58
Hundziak, M., 220
Hunt, B. M., 221
Hunter, M. A., 61
Hyman, C. B., 59

Ingram, T. T. S., 25, 26, 27, 29, 43
Ireland, P. E., 61

Jackson, H., 74, 93
Jefferson, T. W., 92
Jerger, J., 58, 61
Jersild, A. T., 255, 260

Kamijo, Y., 59
Kanadani, M., 61
Karlin, I. W., 59

Kass, C. E., 226, 235
Kastein, S., 58, 59
Keaster, J., 59
Kendall, D. C., 58, 61
Kennedy, C., 66, 93
Kephart, N. C., 11, 16, 22, 25, 27, 43, 146, 155, 192, 193, 221, 247
Kirk, S. A., 43, 62, 221, 235, 248, 260
Kiuchi, S., 59
Kleffner, F. R., 59, 61
Knobloch, H., 108, 124, 127
Korn, S., 93

Landau, W. M., 59, 61
Laufer, M. W., 108
Lee, J., 108
Lefever, D. W., 235
Lefford, A., 10
Lehtinen, L., 11, 20, 26, 28, 43, 62, 108, 131, 132, 145, 146, 192, 193, 222, 247
Levi, A., 235
Levine, E. S., 87, 93
Lewis, R. S., 26, 28, 43, 252
Lowell, E. L., 61, 93

Mark, H. J., 59
Maslow, P., 235
Maurer, R., 220
McCammon, G. B., 201, 221
McCarthy, J. J., 43, 62, 221, 260
McCarthy, J. P., 235, 251
McCoy, R. H., 50, 59
McGaughran, L. S., 93
McGinnis, M. A., 251
McHugh, H. E., 50, 51, 54, 55, 56, 59, 62
Merklein, R. A., 62
Metfessel, N. S., 93
Milgram, N. A., 93
Miller, A., 235
Miller, M., 60, 62
Miron, M. S., 93
Money, J., 108
Monsees, E. K., 59, 62
Moran, L. J., 93
Moss, J. W., 62
Mowrer, O. H., 33, 43
Mysak, E. D., 43
Myklebust, H. R., 16, 21, 43, 47, 48, 53, 55, 59, 62, 251

Nicks, D. C., 235

O'Connor, N., 10
Ogiba, Y., 59
Oleron, P., 93
Olson, J. L., 62
O'Neill, J. J., 62
Osgood, C. E., 87, 93, 196
Oyer, H. J., 62

Paine, R. S., 15, 26, 43
Pasamanick, B., 108, 124, 127, 194, 221
Pasnikowski, T., 62
Patterson, R., 221
Penfield, W., 33, 43, 62
Piaget, J., 75
Polisar, I. A., 62
Price, L. L., 62

Ramirez, L. S., 66, 93
Rapin, I., 59, 62
Ratzburg, R. H., 192, 221
Reichstein, J., 29, 43, 59, 62
Richter, C. P., 57
Roberts, L., 43, 62
Robinault, I. P., 15, 42
Rosenstein, J., 62
Ryan, G. M., 58

Saarinen, P., 93
Scheerer, M., 93
Schulman, J., 72
Scott, J. W., 61
Shere, M. O., 62
Sheridan, M. D., 43
Silverman, S. R., 60
Simmons, Q. D., 201, 221

Simpson, D., 192
Sloan, W., 221
Sortini, A. J., 62
Strauss, A. A., 4, 5, 11, 16, 20, 22, 25, 26, 27, 28, 43, 62, 108, 124, 126, 127, 131, 132, 133, 145, 146, 192, 193, 194, 221, 222, 247
Suzuki, T., 49, 59, 63
Switzer, J., 239

Taguchi, K., 63
Tannhauser, M. T., 192, 221
Taylor, E. M., 93
Taylor, I. G., 63, 79, 87
Thomas, A., 93
Thorndike, R. L., 94
Thorne, B., 60
Travis, L. E., 43
Twitchell, T. E., 16, 43

Utley, J., 48, 60

Vernon, M., 56, 60
Vigotsky, L. S., 74, 94

Wepman, J. M., 235
Werner, H., 4, 124, 126, 127, 133, 146, 193, 222
Wernicke, C., 53
Whitehurst, M. W., 63
Whittlesey, J. R. B., 235
Williams, W. G., 63
Withrow, F. B., 49, 60
Wunsch, W. L., 94

Zaner, A., 60

SUBJECT INDEX

A

Adapted testing, concept of, 81-84

Aphasia, 52-53

Arithmetic, training in, 139-142, 202-203
abacus, 141
multiple choice procedures, 140
number concept and perceptual organization, 139-140, 201
number symbols, 141, 204
relational concepts, 142
sequential concepts, 142
sorting and matching of groups, 140, 201
use of aids, 202-203, 213-214
visual spatial system, 139, 143

Arthur Point Scale of Performance Tests, 87

Auditory agnosia, 53

Auditory-autonomic handicap, 195, 211-212
group games to promote sociability, 217-218
remediation for academic work, 213-215
remediation for pre-readiness level, 212-213
remediation for readiness level, 213

Auditory-somatic handicap, 195, 208-209
group games to promote sociability, 217-218
remediation for academic work, 210-211
remediation for pre-readiness level, 209-210
remediation for readiness level, 210

B

Bender Visual-Motor Gestalt Test, 73, 88

Benton Visual Retention Test, 88

Brain damage and cerebral dysfunction,
administrative label, 3
and attention and concentration, 69-70
and concept usage, 74-76
defined medically, 64-66
differential diagnosis, 6, 246
diversity of symptoms, 16-17, 123-124, 248
educational characteristics, 7, 78-79, 91
etiologic basis, 4, 223
and intelligence, 66-69
origins of term, 4
perceptual-behavioral manifestations, 19-24, 131-132, 147-148, 150-151, 194-195, 248
abstract attitude, loss of, 22, 133
activity level, 54, 72-73, 131, 134, 140, 143, 194, 203, 204, 207
automatized activity, 132
catastrophic reaction, 23, 131
clumsiness, 131, 147, 198, 230
disinhibition, 21, 131, 134, 140, 143
distractibility, 21, 54, 70-71, 134, 140, 143
figure-ground, 22, 132, 138, 143
forced responsiveness, 132-133
memory, 23, 204
over-response, 22, 134
perseveration, 20, 54, 132-133, 139, 141-142, 143, 215
rigidity, 23
spatial orientation, 148, 228
stereotypy of verbal behavior, 132
withdrawal, 23-24, 54
and personality, 76-78
and psychological evaluation, 79-92
symptomatologic basis, 4, 5

and visual perception, 73-74, 138, 142, 224, 250

C

Central deafness, 53
Columbia Mental Maturity Scale, 87
Contact skills, 153-154
  grasp, 159-160
  reach, 159
  release, 160-161
Curriculum, 248, 249
  arts and crafts, 257-258
  behavioral tools, 251-252
  informational agenda, 252-254
  language arts, 250-251
  music, 216, 258-259
  physical education, 255-257
  self-actualization, 254-255
  spatial and quantitative understanding and skill, 254

D

Developomental environment, 247, 248, 255
Dimensions of educability, 259-260
  autonomy, 260
  efficiency, 260
  level, 259-260
  range, 259-260
  rate, 259-260
Drever-Collins Performance Scale, 87
Dysacusis, 53

E

Educational achievement, 91-92

F

Finger agnosia, 200
Frosting Developmental Test of Visual Perception, 225, 226, 236, 240-242

G

Games, as aids in learning, 180, 206, 210, 214, 216-218, 233
Gates Basic Reading Tests, 91
Gellner Tests, 195
General educational principles of Strauss and Lehtinen,

anticipatory exploration, 134
delay of response, 135
elimination of irrelevant details, 136
environmental structuring, 135
exericse of controls from within, 135-136
reduction of visual and auditory stimulation, 135
special classes, 136
tactical arrangement of children, 136
task simplification, 134
Gestalt Psychology, 132, 139
Goodenough Draw-A-Man-Test, 87
Grouping of children, 136, 197

H

Hearing,
  anatomical aspects, 44
  educational considerations, 56-57
  impairment in children, 49-50, 258
Hearing, measurement of,
  in adults, 46-47
  in children, 47-49
  in neurologically impaired children, 50-52

I

ITPA, 29, 195-196, 225, 226, 231, 236, 238-239, 242, 251

K

Kohs Blocks, 73, 84

L

Laterality, 168, 231
Learning,
  and experiential deficit, 19, 176
  and perceptual deficit, 19
  and sensory deficit, 19
Leiter International Performance Scale, 87
Locomotion, 152-153, 256
  crawling, 166
  galloping, 166
  jumping, 165
  running, 165
  skipping, 166
  teaching of, 164
  walking, 165

M

Mental retardation,
educable, 259, 260
and emotional maladjustment, 220
endogenous-exogenous, 5, 6, 194, 218
Gellner's types, 194-195
psychiatric aspects, 106-107
and return to community, 219
trainable, 259
Merrill-Palmer Scale of Mental Tests, 87
Metropolitan Achievement Tests, 91
Midbrain, relation to learning handicaps, 194-195
Motor responses, 149-151
motor defect, 175-177
motor generalization, 168-169
teaching of, 169-175
motor patterns, 149-150
motor skills, 149, 230

N

Nebraska Test of Learning Aptitude for Young Deaf Children, 87
Neurological examination,
cerebral cortex, motor strip, 117
corticospinal tract, 117
form and function of central nervous system, 121-122
inferential nature of diagnosis, 111-112, 119, 125-126
peripheral nerve status, 113-114
reflex response, 114-117
Neurotic behavior disorders, 104-105

O

Ocular control, 187-188
ocular fixation, 188-190
ocular pursuit, 190-191, 230, 231
Ontario School Ability Examination, 87
Oral communication,
disorders of, 24, 209, 211
articulation, 26
auditory acuity, 24
auditory perception, 25
grammar, 27
language development, 25, 209
semantics, 27-29
and the teaching process, 17
and thinking, 18
Oral language learning,
association functions, 231
expressive langauge, 231-232
memory for semantic content, 231, 233
pre-propositional stage, 35
propositional stage, 35-36
receptive language, 231
stimulation of, 37-39, 207, 230, 231
theories of, 33
Oral teaching,
speech content considerations, 41-42, 213
speech production considerations, 40-41, 209-210

P

Peabody Picture Vocabulary Test, 87
Perceptual-motor match, 177-179, 188
control of continuous activities, 181-186
control of sequential acts, 186-187
control of single acts, 179-181
eye-hand coordination, 178, 230
Perceptual training, 136-139, 199-201
color cues, 137-138, 143, 145
copying, 184-186
drawing, 183-184, 228
drill versus insight, 139
figure-ground discrimination, 228
Frostig Program, 227
integration with motor learning, 178
matching three dimensional objects to flat copy, 137, 200, 205
oral work, 139
outlining of patterns and contours, 137-138
repetition, 137
short tasks, 139, 205
teacher-and child-constructed materials, 138
touch and feeling sensations, 199-200, 257
tracing, 181-182, 228, 257
use of hands, 199, 257
visual-motor coordination, 228
Posture and maintenance of balance,

151-152, 230, 255
  balance beam as an aid, 155-159
  teaching of, 154-159
Potential competence, concept of, 84-86
Projective tests, 88
Psychiatric diagnosis, as influenced by,
  attitudes of handicapped child, 102-
    103
  communication difficulties, 101
  context of referral, 95
  convulsive disorders, 101
  family context, 102
  muscular difficulties, 100
  time of life of onset of brain injury,
    100
Psychopathic personality, 105

R

Randall's Island Performance Tests, 87
Reactive behavior disorders, 104
Reading, remedial training in, 142-145
  aids to counteract distractibility in
    reading, 144
  analytical versus global approach, 144
  exercises in perception of letters, 143,
    205
  instruction in auditory perception,
    144
  matching words as readiness experi-
    ence, 143
  reading disability, 142, 204
  sound blending, multiple choice tech-
    niques, 144
Receipt and propulsion skills, 154
  teaching of, 161-164, 178
Research Project Number 50 of the
  Columbus State School, 194, 195, 196,
  218
Rorschach Test, 88

S

Schizophrenia, childhood type, 105-107,
  212
Sensory-motor training, 230-231

body awareness, 230-231, 254
  Montessori materials, 231
Stanford Achievement Tests, 91
Stanford-Binet Intelligence Scale, 68, 73,
  74, 82, 83, 85, 87, 218, 219
Strauss Syndrome, 193

T

Thematic apperception tests, 88

V

Visual-autonomic handicap, 195, 203-
  204, 219
  group games to promote sociability,
    217
  remediation for academic work, 207-
    208
  remediation for pre-readiness level,
    204-205
  remediation for readiness level, 205-
    207
Visual-somatic handicap, 195, 198-199
  group games to promote sociability,
    216-217
  remediation for arithmetic, 202-203
  remediation for pre-readiness level,
    199
  remediation for readiness level, 199-
    201
  remediation for reading, 201
  remediation for writing, 202

W

Wechsler Intelligence Scale for Children, 67, 68, 69, 81, 87, 225, 236, 237,
  242
Wepman Test of Auditory Discrimination, 225, 226, 236, 242
Writing, 145, 202
  cursive writing, 145
  enhancement of writing readiness,
    145, 228
  as a means of enhancing reading, 145
  use of aids, 202